PRENTICE-HALL FOUNDATIONS OF MODERN BIOLOGY SERIES

William D. McElroy and Carl P. Swanson, Editors

NEW VOLUME

Chemical Background for the Biological Sciences, Emil H. White

SECOND EDITIONS

The Cell, Carl P. Swanson

Cell Physiology and Biochemistry, William D. McElroy

Heredity, David M. Bonner and Stanley E. Mills

Adaptation, Bruce Wallace and Adrian M. Srb

Growth and Development, Maurice Sussman

Animal Physiology, Knut Schmidt-Nielsen

Animal Diversity, Earl D. Hanson

Animal Behavior, V. G. Dethier and Eliot Stellar

The Life of the Green Plant, Arthur W. Galston

The Plant Kingdom, Harold C. Bold

Man in Nature, Marston Bates

MAURICE SUSSMAN   *Brandeis University*

Englewood Cliffs, N. J.   **PRENTICE-HALL, INC.**

Growth
and Development

SECOND EDITION

FOUNDATIONS OF MODERN BIOLOGY SERIES

Growth and Development, SECOND EDITION, *Maurice Sussman*

FOUNDATIONS OF MODERN BIOLOGY SERIES

William D. McElroy and Carl P. Swanson, Editors

Design by Walter Behnke

Drawings by Felix Cooper

PRENTICE-HALL INTERNATIONAL, INC., *London*

PRENTICE-HALL OF AUSTRALIA, PTY., LTD., *Sydney*

PRENTICE-HALL OF CANADA, LTD., *Toronto*

PRENTICE-HALL FRANCE, S. A. R. L., *Paris*

PRENTICE-HALL OF INDIA PVT. LTD., *New Delhi*

PRENTICE-HALL OF JAPAN, INC., *Tokyo*

PRENTICE-HALL DE MEXICO, S. A., *Mexico City*

C-36561 (p)   *C-36562 (c)*

FOR RAQUEL

Foundations
of Modern Biology
Series

PREFACE TO THE FIRST EDITION

The science of biology today is *not* the same science of fifty, twenty-five, or even ten years ago. Today's accelerated pace of research, aided by new instruments, techniques, and points of view, imparts to biology a rapidly changing character as discoveries pile one on top of the other. All of us are aware, however, that each new and important discovery is not just a mere addition to our knowledge; it also throws our established beliefs into question, and forces us constantly to reappraise and often to reshape the foundations upon which biology rests. An adequate presentation of the dynamic state of modern biology is, therefore, a formidable task and a challenge worthy of our best teachers.

The authors of this series believe that a new approach to the organization of the subject matter of biology is urgently needed to meet this challenge, an approach that introduces the student to biology as a growing, active science, and that also *permits each teacher of biology to determine the level and structure of his own course.* A single textbook cannot provide such flexibility, and it is the author's strong conviction that these student needs and teacher prerogatives can best be met by a series of short, inexpensive, well-written, and well-illustrated books so planned as to encompass those areas of study central to an understanding of the content, state, and direction of modern biology. The FOUNDATIONS OF MODERN BIOLOGY SERIES represents the translation of these ideas into print, with each volume being complete in itself yet at the same time serving as an integral part of the series as a whole.

PREFACE TO THE SECOND EDITION

The first edition of the FOUNDATIONS OF MODERN BIOLOGY SERIES represented a marked departure from the traditions of textbook writing. The enthusiastic acceptance of the Series by teachers of biology, here and abroad, has been most heartening, and confirms our belief that there was a long-felt need for flexible teaching units based on current views and concepts. The second edition of all volumes in the Series retains the earlier flexibility, eliminates certain unnecessary overlaps of content, introduces new and relevant information, and provides more meaningful illustrative material.

The Series has also been strengthened by the inclusion of a new volume, *Chemical Background for the Biological Sciences* by Dr. Emil White. The dependence of modern biology on a sound foundation in physics and chemistry is obvious; this volume is designed to provide the necessary background in these areas.

In preparing the second edition of the Series, the authors and editors gratefully acknowledge the many constructive criticisms that have been made by hundreds of teaching biologists. Their interest and aid have made the task of writing more a pleasure than a burden.

Contents

ix

GROWTH AND DEVELOPMENT

What Is Development?

The essence of life is change. The essence of death is inertia. All of us learn this at an early age. We watch the waxing and waning of the seasons and observe a regular succession of changes in the living things about us. We watch the ant on a blade of grass, the fish in a bowl, the dog in our back yard, and find them in states of ceaseless activity. Some are short-term activities such as moving, eating, excreting, mating; some are long-term activities that become apparent only after the passage of weeks and months. Ultimately, we recognize these changes in ourselves as we grow and develop from babyhood to adulthood.

The biologist takes a more penetrating view of biological activities and distinguishes three classes of alterations:

1. Short-term physiological and morphological alterations. Many of these changes are quite familiar to us. For example, our body temperature may vary from hour to hour depending on whether we are awake or asleep, at work or at rest. The color, texture, and thickness of an animal pelt can vary rather significantly from winter to winter in the life of an

1

animal, depending on the severity of each winter. A callus may form on a hard-working hand and disappear when the hand's owner takes up a more sedentary occupation. Sudden anger may increase the heart beat, divert blood from intestines to muscles, and augment the rate of breathing.

As still another example, if we expose a population of yeast cells that have been grown with glucose as an energy source to a new sugar, maltose, the cells, in order to utilize the maltose, must first synthesize an entirely new enzyme that splits it into usable fragments. They can do this in a relatively short time. If the maltose were removed and replaced by glucose, the new enzyme would disappear from the growing cells and no record would be left of this interlude of physiological change.

All such activities have common properties. They do not occur in any regular rhythm but merely represent sporadic adjustments to specific environmental stimuli. Further, they are usually reversible; that is, the progression of changes leaves the organism neither vastly different from what it was before nor unable to return to its former state.

2. Long-term genetic and evolutionary changes. Alterations in the genetic apparatus of an organism are called *mutations* and are inherited by the offspring. A single mutation may be minute in itself, perhaps leading only to the loss or gain of the capacity to synthesize a single enzyme, and its effect on the form or functioning of the organism may be correspondingly slight. If by virtue of the change, the mutant is more fitted to survive than its unaltered relatives (if it can breed faster, for example), it will flourish and the following generations will probably include a greater proportion of that mutant type. When successive mutations stand the test of natural selection, they can, over many generations, produce a variety of organism greatly different from its distant forebears. In the aggregate, these progressions contribute to the evolution of species.

Note how different these evolutionary changes are from the short-term changes mentioned before. First of all, a much longer time is involved, for the appearance of a new variety of organism in large numbers may require many generations of growth and reproduction. Second, the biologist who studies these phenomena must examine populations, not individual organisms, in order to follow the spread of genetic changes.

3. Developmental events. Developmental events are seen most dramatically in the growth patterns of higher animals. A fertilized egg undergoes an orderly series of changes to become an embryo. The embryo develops further into the young animal, which in turn matures into an adult. The adult reaches its peak and then experiences a series of degenerative changes that ultimately lead to death. At maturity the animal releases eggs or sperm that originate yet another cycle of development.

The tempo of these phenomena is too slow to be included in the first category described above and too fast for the second. Moreover, the changes are progressive; that is, they occur in a regular sequence with little variation, each leaving the organism different from its former state and unable to return to it. They begin before birth and end shortly after death, and in toto they represent the life cycle of the organism.

Developmental phenomena are not restricted to higher plants and animals. Even the single cell goes through a corresponding progression of changes. Its life cycle begins when it arises from the division of its parent into daughters and ends when it in turn divides. Between times, it grows in size and protoplasmic content, synthesizes cellular constituents in an orderly and well-regulated manner, and can, indeed, develop new *organelles* (a term used to designate any of the organized structures of a cell), and change its form and functioning drastically.

Unorganized populations of cells also show developmental phenomena. For example, a culture of microorganisms has a life cycle of its own, as contrasted with those of the individual cells of which it is composed. As will be described in detail later, when we add an inoculum of bacteria to nutrient broth, the culture goes through an orderly succession of well-defined growth stages, reaches a stationary state, and ultimately passes into a period of decline during which the cells degenerate and die. Thus the bacteria en masse act in much the same fashion as the cells of a higher organism except that they are loosely distributed and largely independent, whereas the cells of higher forms are dependent on each other and exist within compact organized structures. In fact, some microorganisms live for part of their life cycles as independent cells, and during the remainder actually do come together and construct organized multicellular structures.

THE CENTRAL PROBLEMS OF DEVELOPMENTAL BIOLOGY

As we consider the life cycles mentioned above, three central problems of development become apparent. We shall take them up here.

Growth

An egg starts as a single microscopic cell with one nucleus and by growth and replication produces an adult containing millions of cells. Needless to say, this represents a many-millionfold increase in protoplasmic mass. A number of questions come to mind when we think about this phenomenon. How is growth initiated? What raw materials are required for the synthesis of protoplasm? What specific chemical reactions lead to the formation of nuclei, enzymes, cell walls, etc.? From where does an organism draw the energy needed to carry out these syntheses? Why does growth stop?

Another significant attribute of growth is that all the parts of an organism increase in a carefully regulated manner. That is, if a cell doubles its size, the size of the nucleus, cytoplasmic constituents, cell wall, etc., all increase in proportion to one another. As a boy grows into a man, his organs increase harmoniously. Thus, the length of his arm bears a fixed relation to his height, and within rather close limits this same relation holds in all other boys. There must, therefore, be regulatory mechanisms in cells and organisms that govern such relationships. What are these mechanisms?

Cellular Differentiation

The millions of cells descended from the original fertilized egg are not all the same. Some are skin cells, others are nerve cells, still others are muscle cells, etc. They look different and perform decidedly different functions. When we think about the reproduction of, say, a bacterium or a rabbit, we normally expect the descendents of each to look and act very much like, if not the same as, the original bacterium or rabbit. Such is not the case, however, for the descendants of developing cells in an embryo. The processes by which these cells become specialized are collectively called *cellular differentiation*. These processes are still largely unknown and present a major challenge to developmental biologists.

Another mysterious aspect of cellular differentiation is the way the numbers of each cell type are carefully regulated. For example, you will never find an embryo with too many brain cells and too few liver cells or vice versa. Here again, as in the case of the boy and his arm, the various tissues and organs of the body bear a relatively fixed relation to one another. The mechanisms that control the proportions of differentiated cells are still to be discovered.

Morphogenesis

A multicellular organism is not simply a bag of cells thrown together helter skelter. It is composed of organs and tissues, and, as has been mentioned, the parts of the animal are arranged in a specific pattern and bear definite relations to one another in terms of size and cellular content. Morphological regulation extends to the individual cell and its organelles. The establishment of this pattern and the processes whereby the adult organism takes its final shape is termed *morphogenesis* and requires explanation in physical and chemical terms.

THE RELATIONSHIP OF DEVELOPMENTAL BIOLOGY
TO OTHER BIOLOGICAL DISCIPLINES

As we consider the various aspects of developmental biology in detail in later chapters, it will become obvious that this subject does not exist apart from the other biological disciplines. Development involves changes in the basic structure of an organism. Thus, a rigorous description of developmental events requires excursions into gross and microscopic anatomy, into histology (which deals with tissue composition), and into cytology (which deals with cell structure). And, since changes in the structure of an organism are brought about by new combinations of biochemical reactions and the new structure leads in turn to further changes in function, biochemistry and physiology must be included in developmental study. Finally, because development does involve change, it bears a direct relation to genetics. For example, when cellular differentiation occurs—i.e., when a single egg cell gives rise to a galaxy of cell types: nerve, muscle, skin, cartilage cells—we want to know if the genetic constitutions of these cells had to change in order to permit them to look and act differently, and if so, what the nature of the change was.

As you see then, developmental studies are intimately involved with the rest of biology, and scientists who deal with developmental problems in their research must bring many different kinds of skills and training to bear upon such problems.

The Growth
and Reproduction
of Single Cells

As mentioned in Chapter 1, the life cycle of a single cell starts when it arises from its mother and ends when it in turn produces daughters. It therefore faces, first, the task of synthesizing new cell constituents, sufficient in quantity and kind, to equip its daughters for their own cycles of growth and reproduction. Second, it must divide the proceeds among them equitably so as to produce normal, well-functioning progeny.*

VARIETIES OF CELL DIVISION

Nature has found several good solutions to the problem of sharing so that different methods of cell division are employed by various types of organisms (see Fig. 2-1).

1. Fission. In this type, the parent cell grows to approximately twice its original size and then splits into two more or less equal daughter cells. Protozoan and animal cells divide in this fashion. They simply constrict in the middle

* See Chapter 8 for a more detailed discussion of these matters.

6

and the two halves pull apart. Bacterial and plant cells also reproduce by fission, but they have rigid walls and divide by constructing a cross wall.

2. Budding. The mother cell forms a little bleb at the surface, which grows rapidly to the approximate size of the mother and finally constricts off. It may separate completely from the mother or may remain attached. In the latter case, both mother and daughter may bud and so produce a chain of cells. This is the manner in which yeast cells divide.

3. Growth of filaments. The cells of fungi and some algae are linked together in thin hair-like fibers. Since growth can occur only at the tip of each filament, the tip elongates and a cross wall forms to yield a cell with a growing tip on its far end. Branching often occurs, when the growing tip bifurcates and both branches elongate in separate strands.

4. Fragmentation. The animal parasite *Plasmodium malariae* which grows inside red blood cells, is one of a number of microorganisms that reproduce by fragmentation. The parent nucleus divides into as many as 24 daughter nuclei and the cytoplasm coalesces about each of them. Separate walls are formed around the conglomerates of nucleus and cytoplasm, which are now called *merozoites*. The host red cell ruptures and releases the merozoites, each of which can now infect another red blood cell.

Fig. 2-1. Asexual reproduction. (1) Fission as it occurs in amebae and bacteria. (2) Budding in yeast. (3) Filamentous growth in molds. (4) Fragmentation in Plasmodium malariae. (5) Noncellular growth in the myxomycetes.

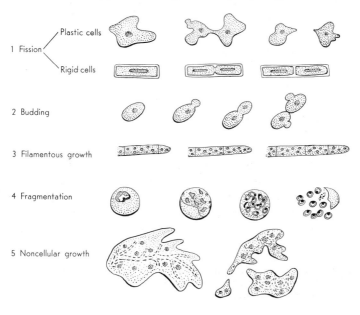

(Incidentally, the well-known chills and fever of malaria are associated with the simultaneous release of merozoites from many blood cells.) The term fragmentation is a bit misleading because the parent organism does not break up into incomplete fragments, each of which reconstitutes a whole new organism. Rather it is as if a bacterium would synthesize enough protoplasm to create many new cells instead of just two. Many kinds of molds, algae, and protozoa form large numbers of spores * at certain stages of their life cycles. In principle, the process resembles that of *Plasmodium malariae.*

5. Noncellular growth. A few organisms can grow extensively without cell division. A group called the mycetozoa consists of ameboid masses of protoplasm that contain many nuclei. The protoplasm increases in amount and the nuclei divide as the organisms grow. Each protoplasmic mass sometimes fragments (in the true sense) to yield two or more smaller masses. It should be noted that some higher animals can also fragment into small pieces, each of which can then reconstitute a whole new organism. Flatworms, starfish, and many others do this.

Nuclear Division

All plant and animal and most microbial cells contain nuclei, i.e., membrane-bounded organelles containing DNA which is organized into one or more chromosomes. Even though bacteria and blue-green algae do not contain discrete nuclei separated from the other cell constituents by a membrane, they do contain DNA organized into chromosome-like structures which are concentrated within the cells into masses called nucleoids. Among them all it is an invariable rule that cell division is preceded by the division of the nuclei (or nucleoids) into daughters.

The primary method of vegetative nuclear division is that of *mitosis.* The particular stages need not concern us here.† The significance of mitosis is that it is an almost foolproof way of ensuring that each daughter nucleus will possess a copy of each chromosome and, therefore, a complete set of the genetic material contained therein.

Not all nuclei divide by mitosis, however. In some cells the nucleus does not assume the mitotic configuration, but merely stretches out into a dumbbell shape. The dumbbell constricts in the middle and the two daughter nuclei pinch apart. That is called *amitosis.* Amitotic division is restricted to a few microorganisms and (rarely) cells of higher animals. As you may know, certain tissue cells grow only in the young animal and

---

* Special cells with thick walls that resist drying, heat, and radiation and that can lie dormant for long periods of time until permitted to germinate.

† See C. P. Swanson, *The Cell,* 2nd ed. (Englewood Cliffs, N. J.: Prentice-Hall, 1964), for a detailed description of mitosis.

cease dividing in the adult, and it is interesting to note that their last few divisions are sometimes amitotic. Degenerating or abnormal tissue cells (e.g., tumors) also may divide amitotically on occasion.

Extranuclear Elements

Some organelles of the cell seem to be partly or completely independent of the nucleus. For example, the long whip-like flagellum seem in many protozoa ·is formed from a small granule at its base called a blepharoblast or basal granule. When certain protozoa divide, the old flagellum disappears and the basal granule appears to split in two. Each daughter cell receives a daughter granule and at the completion of cell division each granule forms a new flagellum. If by mischance one of the daughter cells does not receive a basal granule, it and its descendants will never again form a flagellum. Thus, the basal granule is independent of the nucleus to the extent that the latter cannot replace the former after it once has been lost.

Other organelles (the gullets of ciliate protozoa, the chloroplasts of some algae, etc.) act in the same fashion, i.e., they duplicate prior to cell division and if lost from a cell cannot be regained. A most interesting case involves the mitochondria of yeast. Mitochondria are small bodies enclosed in membranes and distributed in the cytoplasm. They contain organized collections of enzymes involved in respiration. Recently it has been found that normally large yeast cells, which can respire, occasionally give rise by budding to dwarf cells, which cannot respire. And the descendants of these so-called "petite" cells are invariably petite even after hundreds of generations of growth. Thus, once lost, the capacity to respire can never be regained. During budding, the mitochondria are normally shared between mother and daughter cell, but once in a while by mistake the bud receives none of them. Because these mitochondria seem to be independent, in the same sense as are flagellar granules, a cell bereft of them cannot respire nor can its descendants do so, the loss being irretrievable.

The nucleus itself, of course, is an autonomous organelle. That is, a cell deprived of its nucleus cannot create a new one. The loss of the nucleus is lethal for the cell; when anucleate, it can no longer reproduce.

In summary, the cell is not simply a bag of homogeneous material parcelled out in imprecise fashion during cell division. It is an assembly of highly structured organelles. Many of these (nucleus, basal granules, etc.) are autonomous in the sense that they control their own duplication. Thus, for cell division to leave the daughters with a fair share of all the constituents, a cell must make coordinated preparations, and organelles must be moved to the right places in the mother cell.

CONTROL OF BIOCHEMICAL EVENTS
DURING THE CELL DIVISION CYCLE

In recent years, biologists have begun to study the succession of biochemical events during the cell division cycle. Some have refined analytical techniques to the point where they can study a single cell, weigh it (despite having to deal with weights of only millionths of a gram), and, by microchemical analysis, determine the amounts of the cell constituents (even though these are present in infinitesimal quantities). Other biologists have devised conditions to make cell populations divide synchronously. Cell populations are usually asynchronous; that is, at any instant some will be preparing to divide, some will have just completed division, and others will be in an intermediate stage. With synchronized cells, we need not apply very delicate and sensitive techniques for the study of a single cell, but instead can work with large samples of cells and thereby examine more easily the biochemical and morphological events that accompany each stage of the division cycle. This work has only begun, but ultimately we may hope to understand how the cell coordinates the synthesis of all its constituents. It is already clear from such studies that various cell constituents are synthesized during very specific phases of the division cycle. Figure 2-2 illustrates schematically the formation of deoxyribose nucleic acid (DNA), the primary component of chromosomes and the bearer of the cell's genetic constitution, as it occurs in most animal and plant cells. As you can see, the DNA is synthesized during a relatively short period between successive mitoses. Contrary to what you might expect, no DNA is formed during the period when the chromosomes actually divide.

The ability of a cell to precisely control the *time, place,* and *quantity* of DNA synthesis is perhaps most clearly shown in a small ciliate Protozoan called *Euplotes.* This organism, illustrated in Fig. 2-3, has a small micronucleus and a long tape-like macronucleus. The first divides by mitosis. The second, containing many copies of each chromosome, divides amitotically, simply by pinching apart in the middle. Both nuclei divide a few minutes before the start of cell division itself. The actual synthesis of DNA occurs long before the nuclear divisions, however (see Fig. 2-4). In the case of the micronucleus, DNA synthesis starts at the close of the previous nuclear division, continues thereafter for 3 hours, and stops when the DNA content has exactly doubled. Only then does DNA synthesis begin in the macronucleus and this continues for 10 hours until its DNA content has doubled. Both nuclei then remain quiescent for one hour, after which they divide immediately prior to the next cell division. Thus, though the supply of the raw materials and energy needed for DNA synthesis is available to both nuclei in common, the "control switches" for this synthesis are separate and are turned on and off at different times.

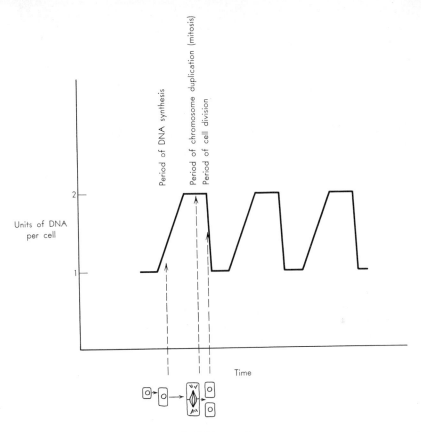

Period of DNA synthesis

Period of chromosome duplication (mitosis)

Period of cell division

Units of DNA per cell

Time

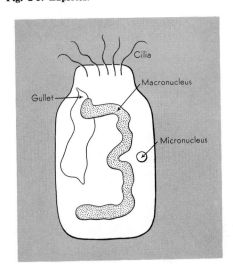

Fig. 2-2. DNA synthesis during the cell division cycle.

Fig. 2-3. Euplotes.

Cilia

Macronucleus

Gullet

Micronucleus

Spatial and temporal controls also operate within the macronucleus itself. At the start of DNA synthesis two bands appear at the ends and begin to move in toward the middle at the same rate. These bands are areas in which the concentrations of nuclear materials differ sharply from adjacent areas and therefore show up optically. It takes 10 hours for the bands to meet in the middle of the macronucleus, i.e., at the time DNA synthesis is complete. The bands are themselves the zones of actual DNA synthesis. Thus, all the DNA in back of each band has already been duplicated; all the DNA

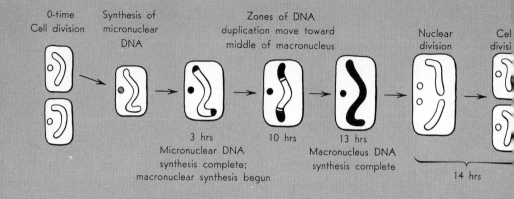

Fig. 2-4. The cycle of DNA synthesis in Euplotes.

in front has not yet been duplicated; and the DNA within the area of the band at any instant is in the process of duplicating itself. Finally, the synthesis of ribose nucleic acid (RNA), which serves as the templates for the formation of proteins, is mutually exclusive from that of DNA, i.e., within the macronucleus, RNA synthesis goes on continuously *except* in the zone where at any instant DNA is being made.

The biochemical pathway leading to DNA synthesis as it is presently understood is reviewed in Fig. 2-5.* The immediate precursors of DNA are the deoxyriboside triphosphates of four different purine and pyrimidine bases (adenine, guanine, cytosine, and thymine). These are knitted together into strands of DNA by an enzyme called *DNA-polymerase*, which uses previously synthesized DNA as a *primer*, or *template*, much as one

* For a fuller discussion of DNA replication, please see the companion volumes by W. D. McElroy, *Cell Physiology and Biochemistry*, 2nd ed., and D. M. Bonner and S. E. Mills, *Heredity*, 2nd ed. (both Englewood Cliffs, N. J.: Prentice-Hall, 1964).

Fig. 2-5. The pathway of DNA synthesis.

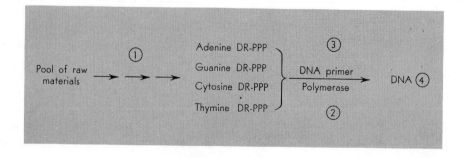

might cut material for a dress according to a previously made pattern. The sequence of purine and pyrimidine bases along the newly synthesized chains of DNA is determined by the corresponding sequences in the primer, thereby insuring accurate duplication. A priori, we can envision four levels at which DNA synthesis might be controlled. These are:

1. *Supply of precursors.* If the precursors were made available only at certain periods of the cell division cycle, DNA synthesis could occur only at those times.

2. *Activity of the polymerase.* If the enzyme itself were made available only at certain periods of the division cycle, synthesis would be restricted to these periods.

3. *Physical state of the DNA primer.* It is known that, in a test tube, the priming DNA must be in a very special physical state in order for it to act as a template for DNA synthesis. Thus, control over new DNA synthesis might be exerted through changes in the physical state of the old DNA.

4. *Control by the product.* Some properties of the newly synthesized DNA might restrict further synthesis.

Current research in this field is directed toward finding out the level (or levels) that actually do control DNA synthesis in living cells and toward identifying the nature of these controls. I have gone into this particular aspect of the cell division cycle in great detail in order that you might gain an appreciation of (a) the complicated task of finding out what controls the operation of even this one part of the cell's economy and (b) the depths of our present ignorance of this subject and the amount of work yet to be done. It should be realized that the sequence of events leading to cell division must also involve similar programs for the synthesis of RNA and proteins as well as all the minor cell constituents, and these reactions must also be controlled *spatially, temporally,* and *quantitatively.*

The Growth
of Cell
Populations

CHAPTER THREE

How a population of cells grows, and the processes, both internal and external, that control and limit growth are fundamental biological problems. A wide variety of living organisms has served as objects of study. Much has been learned by examining the growth of populations of microorganisms —bacteria, protozoa, algae, and fungi. In recent years, biologists have been able to remove tissues of higher animals and plants and grow them outside the body (tissue culture). In some cases, it has been possible to disaggregate such tissues and to cultivate the cells as dispersed individuals exactly as if they were microorganisms. Even the cells of human beings (tumor cells, kidney cells, etc.) can be so treated, and in the process they have been found to obey the same rules of growth and nutrition as their more primitive brethren. Intact higher animals have been grown under controlled conditions in which the natural diet is replaced by mixtures of known chemical compounds delivered in measured amounts. The rat is a favorite laboratory animal for this purpose, but other animals such as the fruit fly (*Drosophila*) and the university undergraduate have been used.

14

The term "growth" has at least two meanings and a cell population may grow in one sense but not in another. Growth, under one interpretation, is an increase in the number of cells, which is found by counting the total population or a measured sample from it. Growth can also be described as an increase in protoplasmic material, which we find by measuring changes in weight or volume. Or we can pick out as a criterion some constituent of protoplasm that is always a constant proportion of the whole, such as the nitrogen content or protein content. If either were to increase, we would know to what extent the total protoplasmic mass had increased.

It should be noted that both cell number and protoplasmic content do not always increase together. For instance, cell division can occur without any increase in protoplasm; the result is a greater number of smaller cells. Alternatively, protoplasm can be synthesized in the absence of cell division, in which case the cells grow larger but not more numerous. However, isolated growth of these kinds can go on only under exceptional conditions and for a relatively short time. Ultimately cell division must cease without protoplasmic increase and vice versa.

NUTRITION

The process of growth, involving an increase in protoplasm, requires the synthesis of a wide variety of cell constituents—nuclei including chromosomal material, centrioles, nucleoli, etc.; mitochondria and other cytoplasmic organelles; thousands of enzyme molecules; cell membranes and other structural material. These require the synthesis of macromolecules such as proteins, nucleic acids, and polysaccharides in which many subunits are linked together. The subunits themselves—amino acids, sugars, fatty acids, vitamins, etc.—must be synthesized from still simpler compounds or must be assimilated from the environment.

Two basic needs must be met if these activities are to be accomplished —the need for energy and the need for raw materials. Cells obtain energy by the oxidation of materials obtained from the environment. Sugars are the prime fuels for this purpose, but many other oxidizable compounds can be employed by one or another kind of cell. The energy thus made available is employed for the synthetic reactions.

At their simplest levels, the raw materials for the synthesis of protoplasm are the elements of which cells are composed. The major components are carbon, hydrogen, oxygen, nitrogen, sulfur, phosphorus, magnesium, manganese, and iron, and there are traces of many other elements as well. All these elements must be supplied in usable form. For example, the amino acid alanine, $CH_3CH_2NH_2COOH$, is essential for the synthesis of proteins. Yet no known organism can synthesize alanine if it is merely supplied with elemental carbon, hydrogen, oxygen, and nitrogen.

But some bacteria can do so by converting nitrogen from the air to ammonia and combining the ammonia with pyruvic acid as follows:

$$NH_3 + 2H + CH_3CO\ COOH \longrightarrow CH_3CHNH_2COOH + H_2O$$

Other cells cannot convert N_2 to NH_3, but if given NH_3 and pyruvic acid they can make alanine. Still other cells, which do not possess any of the enzymes that catalyze these reactions, must be supplied with alanine itself if they are to grow. The diversity of nutritional requirements results from the inability of cells to synthesize one or another protoplasmic constituent.

The extent of this diversity may be appreciated by comparing the constituents of two different culture media, one used for the cultivation of the bacterium *Escherichia coli* and the other for the growth of human tumor cells in dispersed culture (Table 3-1). The latter medium includes a great number of amino acids and vitamins that are absent in the former. Yet *E. coli* cells contain all of these compounds. The difference is that the bacteria can synthesize them using glucose and ammonium chloride as raw materials whereas the tumor cells cannot and therefore must be supplied with the preformed material.

Table 3-1

NUTRITIONAL REQUIREMENTS OF *ESCHERICHIA COLI*
AND OF HUMAN TUMOR (HeLa) CELLS

E. Coli:
1. Glucose (source of energy and carbon)
2. Ammonium chloride (source of nitrogen)
3. Inorganic salts, i.e., $MgSO_4$, KH_2PO_4, NaCl, etc.
4. Water

HeLa Cells:
1. Glucose
2. Amino acids (arginine, histidine, lysine, tryptophan, phenylalanine, methionine, threonine, leucine, isoleucine, valine, glutamic acid, aspartic acid, proline, glycine, glutamine, tyrosine, cystine)
3. Vitamins (thiamine, riboflavin, pyridoxine, folic acid, biotin, choline, pantothenic acid, nicotinamide, inositol, hypoxanthine, vitamin B-12)
4. Inorganic salts
5. Proteins (fetuin and serum albumin) *
6. Water

* The two proteins included in the tissue culture medium are not nutrients but satisfy certain physical requirements of these tumor cells for growth outside the body.

THE S-SHAPED CURVE OF GROWTH

Figure 3-1 shows growth curves that, as you can see, are S-shaped. The abscissa is time—minutes, days, hours, years, depending on the organisms studied. The ordinate is growth and can describe the number of cells in a bacterial culture, the number of human beings on earth, the size or

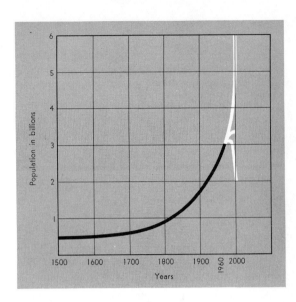

Fig. 3-1A. The growth curve of the human population of the world.

Fig. 3-1B. Growth of the chick during its embryonic and post-hatching periods. (Redrawn from Weiss and Kavanau.)

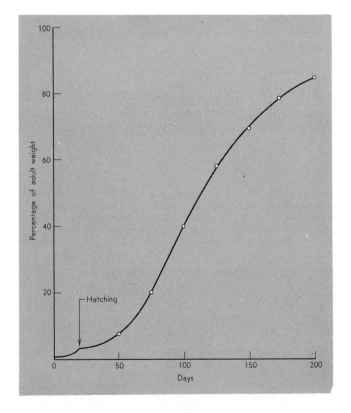

weight of a sunflower seedling or a rat, the size or weight of the heart or the brain. In other words, the ordinate is a measure of the growth of a population or a single multicellular organism or any of its parts and, when growing under optimal conditions, all show precisely this sort of growth curve. Many questions come to mind when we look at this curve. Why does growth start? Why does it stop? Why is the curve S-shaped?

In this discussion of the factors affecting growth, we shall deal with a culture of bacteria because it is easy to understand, and because conclusions reached from such studies are applicable to all organisms, plant and animal alike.

Imagine that we introduce a few hundred bacterial cells into a cotton-stoppered flask containing sterile, nutrient broth (called the "medium"). Every hour or so we abstract one cubic centimeter of the broth and determine the number of living bacterial cells. Figure 3-1C shows the complete curve that would be obtained.

The curve is divided into three parts: I—the period called the *lag phase,* during which the cells prepare for growth; II—the period of actual growth, called the *exponential or logarithmic phase;* III—the period in which growth ceases and the population enters the *stationary phase.* None of these phases is of set duration. That is to say, the time a culture spends in each phase depends on the particular species of bacteria and the conditions under which they are grown.

Lag Phase

The lag phase is a period of rapid protoplasmic growth and a period of preparation for the cell division that is to come. Thus, it is a time when the cells become larger but remain constant in number.

We may ask why cells must prepare for cell division. Why can they

Fig. 3-1C. Bacteria are introduced into fresh nutrient broth. At intervals, a sample is abstracted to determine the number of bacteria per cubic centimeter of broth. Three phases of the resultant growth curve are recognized: I—lag phase; II—logarithmic phase; III—stationary phase. If, now, bacteria from the stationary phase are used to inoculate another flask of nutrient broth, the growth pattern repeats itself.

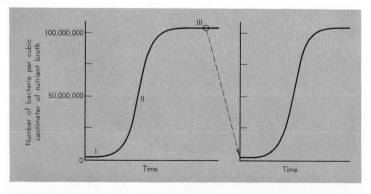

not enter the exponential phase immediately? The answer is that a cell in the exponential phase is somewhat like an assembly line operating full-blast. Parts are fabricated on the line in consecutive stages or are received from outside contractors and these are ultimately put together to yield the finished product. The prime requirement for an efficient assembly line is that all the operations mesh harmoniously. Supplies must arrive in the right place, at the right time, and in the right amounts, and the operations along the assembly line must proceed at equivalent speeds. If, then, we start a culture with cells that are already in the exponential phase (i.e., the "assembly lines" are already set up and operative) and supply them with everything they need, the lag phase should be eliminated, and this is just the result that is obtained. In contrast, if we start a culture with cells that are not in the exponential phase, they require time to prepare for growth. We shall now take up the preparations that are necessary to generate the exponential phase.

RESYNTHESIS OF ENZYME SYSTEMS REQUIRED FOR GROWTH. A cell that has already passed the exponential phase is no longer faced with the problems of growing, only with those of survival; it must protect itself against metabolic waste products and other toxic substances that may have built up in the environment, and it must conserve whatever raw materials and energy that it still may have left. In so doing, it may lose some enzymes that are no longer needed and synthesize others that are required for its survival. If such cells are now exposed to a fresh nutrient medium in which growth is once again possible and survival is no longer a problem, they must reverse the course of events mentioned above. But this shift involves extensive protoplasmic reorganization and a further synthesis of enzymes and other macromolecules. All this takes time; hence the lag phase.

THE SYNTHESIS OR ASSIMILATION OF RAW MATERIALS FOR GROWTH. Each original cell must stock up on the chemical subunits (amino acids, sugars, fatty acids, vitamins, etc.) that are needed to construct enough protoplasm to make two cells. If the nutrient supply were rich and these compounds already present in the environment, the job would be simple and the lag phase correspondingly short. If the nutrient supply were poor, the missing subunits would have to be synthesized from simpler materials in the environment. The job, then, would be more difficult and the lag phase correspondingly longer. The lag phase can also depend on how many cells are actually present, for each is a little factory geared to the production of the subunits, and the more factories there are, the faster they can be synthesized and the shorter will be the preparatory period. In the jargon of the bacteriologist, the cells "condition the medium." Moreover, like a well-functioning assembly line, each original cell that has stocked up on enough subunits to create two new cells also insures the continuity of supply so that the two in turn will, without delay, be able to collect or synthesize enough subunits to make four, and so on. Thus, no further lag is apparent and growth can proceed apace. To summarize, then, the lag phase is influenced by:

1. The richness of the nutrient supply.
2. The number of cells preparing for growth.
3. The "physiological state" of the cells.

The Exponential Phase

We now come to the stage of active growth and reproduction and the peculiar S-shaped curve. To understand this stage we need merely consider the properties of populations that are growing actively under optimal conditions:

1. The more organisms there are, the more there can be. In other words, offspring must have parents and the more parents, the more offspring.
2. Most of the organisms in such a population reproduce during their life cycles. Very few are barren.
3. The generation time is constant. That is, the time for each organism to emerge, mature, and reproduce is approximately the same as long as the population continues to grow.

To return to our bacterial culture, the above statements mean (1) that during the exponential phase each bacterial cell gives rise to two, the two to four, the four to eight, etc., and (2) that it takes the same amount of time for one to yield two as for two to yield four, etc. Suppose the generation time were one hour. Then the population would, on the average, double once every hour. If we draw a graph in which the number of cells is plotted against time, we get the curve shown in Fig. 3-2. This is the first part of the S-shaped curve. Now if the period of active growth draws gradually to a close—cells begin to die rather than reproduce and those that can reproduce take longer than an hour to do so—the second part of the S-shaped curve appears.

If growth were unlimited, the growth curve would simply go up and up at an ever increasing rate, and it is interesting to speculate about what would happen to our planet if the growth of, say, bacteria were unlimited. One species of bacteria, *Escherichia coli,* can divide every 20 minutes in an optimal environment. Thus, if at time zero there were one cell, at 20 minutes there would be 2, at 40 minutes 4, at 60 minutes 8, and so on. The series 1, 2, 4, 8 can be expressed as 2^0 (=1); 2^1 (=2); 2^2 (=4);

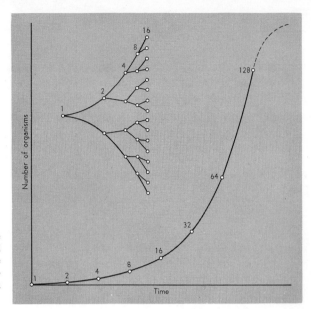

Fig. 3-2. The first part of the S-shaped curve is generated when every organism gives rise to progeny (in this case by binary fission) and the generation time is constant.

2^3 (=8); note that the exponents represent the number of generations of growth that have occurred. Therefore, the number of cells present after n generations of growth would be 2^n. Since the generation time of *Escherichia coli* is 20 minutes, there could be 3 generations per hour, or $24 \times 3 = 72$ generations per day. In other words, were growth not limited, one bacterial cell would give rise in 24 hours to $2^{72} = 40,000,000,000,000,000,000,000$ cells. A mass of bacterial cells this size would weigh 8 million pounds. We would quite literally be up to our ears in bacteria.*

Table 3-2

TIME FOR ORGANISMS TO DOUBLE THEIR MASS

Escherichia coli	20 min
Fly larva	13 hr
Silk worm	68 hr
Rabbit at birth	6 days
Pig at birth	6–7 days
Sheep at birth	10 days
Guinea pig at birth	18 days
Horse at birth	60 days
Man at birth	180 days

The same arguments hold for higher animals. As anyone knows who has had experience with rabbits, they may differ from bacteria to the extent that you need at least two (of the appropriate sexes) to get more, but they are the same as bacteria in that the more rabbits you have the more rabbits you will surely get. Therefore, rabbit colonies or any other

* See the section at the end of the chapter for a detailed discussion of growth kinetics.

animal population, when well fed and given enough space, display S-shaped curves of growth. It should be noted that two rabbits do not necessarily, and in fact hardly ever do, produce only four rabbits and four only eight. The fact that with each generation the number of organisms more than doubles would not change the shape of the curve but would merely make it steeper.

The Stationary Phase

As already mentioned, toward the end of the exponential curve, more and more cells begin to die and those that survive take longer and longer to reproduce. Ultimately the rate of cell death increases so much and the rate of cell growth decreases so much that cells die as fast as new ones appear and the total number of living cells remains constant. This is the stationary phase.

Why does the population stop growing? What limits growth? There are at least two general causes:

1. The supply of an essential nutrient becomes exhausted. If an organism requires a particular nutrient for growth and the supply gives out, the organism will cease growing no matter how much there remains of any other nutrient. Whether the exhausted nutrient happens to be a vitamin, or an amino acid, or a source of energy, or a metal ion, or oxygen, the result will be the same. The cessation of growth may be subtle, as in a bacterial culture, or very dramatic, as when populations of Alaskan lemmings exhaust their food supply and in the course of frantic migration commit mass sucide by leaping into the ocean.

2. The environment becomes too toxic for further growth. Organisms, as they grow, pour out metabolic waste products and thus pollute the environment. As long as the number of organisms is small, the concentration of wastes will be low and will not poison them. When the number is large, the rate of waste production will rise and the concentration in the environment will increase to a toxic level and lower the vitality of the organisms to the extent that they can no longer grow or perhaps even survive.

We should mention a special case under this second category that is particularly pertinent for animal populations, namely the stoppage of growth not by toxic materials but by epidemics caused by parasites. Epidemics are like nuclear chain reactions. That is, the host population must rise above a critical density before the epidemic can take place. (Can you construct an explanation of this?) Thus, when an animal population does grow to great numbers, an epidemic can strike and reduce the population drastically. Then another cycle of growth will begin. Biologists have indeed charted such growth cycles as this for a good many wild animal populations.

GROWTH OF THE MULTICELLULAR ORGANISM

A population of microorganisms is a collection of discrete cells that are largely independent of each other for their existence. The higher animal or plant is itself a collection of discrete cells that is organized into a compact whole, but the cells are closely dependent on one another for their continued existence. To the degree that the animal or plant is simply a collection of discrete cells, it grows according to the same rules as does a microbial culture. But the interdependence of the cells brings complications:

1. All parts of the multicellular organism do not grow at the same rate. Some tissues do not grow at all once the embryo is formed. Others grow very slowly. Still others grow very rapidly. The total organism, however, which is the resultant of all the individual cells and tissues, does grow precisely as do populations of microorganisms, i.e., in an S-shaped curve.

2. All parts of the organism do not stop growing simultaneously. In fact, some tissues continue to grow during the entire lifetime of the animal. However, the total organismic mass does remain relatively constant once maturity is reached (in the absence of pathological changes).

3. The growth of one part of an animal can be and usually is controlled by the activities of another part. A prime example of this is the dependence of many tissues upon secretions of the pituitary gland.

"INDETERMINATE" GROWTH IN MULTICELLULAR ORGANISMS

The manner in which growth in a multicellular system can be confined to special groups of cells in special places is illustrated by a pattern called *indeterminate growth* which occurs in practically all plants and in some animals as well.

The pattern is demonstrated in the following experiment (Figure 3-3). A corn root is cultivated under conditions permitting periodic observation of its length. Marks are made with India ink at equal (1 millimeter) distances along it. Further growth of the root alters the spacing considerably, as shown. The marks placed at or near the tip become widely separated whereas those in the basal portions of the root retain their original spacing. It follows therefore that the root does not grow uniformly along its length but only at the tip. This conclusion is confirmed when the root is examined microscopically. Three zones can be distinguished in which the cells act in decidedly different ways:

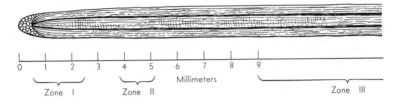

The root at zero time

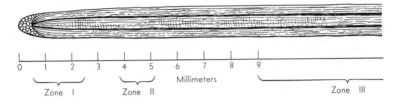

```
0   1   2   3   4   5   6   7   8   9
                      Millimeters
  Zone  I      Zone  II              Zone  III
```

Fig. 3-3. Indeterminate growth in the corn root.

Zone I (0.5–2.5 mm from the apex) in which the cells grow and divide at a high rate.

Zone II (4–5 mm from the apex) in which cells do not divide but do increase markedly in size.

Zone III (9 mm from the apex) in which the cells no longer divide or increase in size.

In this case growth is clearly restricted to a narrow zone within the root. Furthermore, it should be recognized that the same cells are not doing all the growing all the time. As new cells appear and the root elongates, the zone of cell division also moves, and as cells leave the zone (or rather as the zone moves away from particular cells) they cease to divide.

Plant shoots grow in the same manner and growth zones can also be observed in certain primitive "plant-like" animals. Note also the similarity of this pattern to that of the filamentous growth of fungi (Chapter 2).

Many organs of vertebrate animals grow in similar fashion. A particularly clear example is offered by the hair follicle schematically illustrated in Fig. 3–4. Four zones of cellular activity can be distinguished. Zone A is a region of rapid cell division; Zone B is a region of cell elongation and enlargement; in Zone C small fibrils of keratin are synthesized; and,

Fig. 3-4. Growth of a hair follicle.

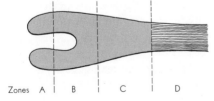

Zones A   B   C   D

as the cells pass into Zone D, the fibrils condense into ordered fibers characteristic of fully formed hair.

THE LIMITATIONS OF SIZE AND FORM

There are obviously great variations in the sizes of living things, particularly between different species but often even within them. Many factors govern size. Among them are the following:

1. Genetic constitution. Mendel did some of his first experiments with the dwarf and giant varieties of pea plants and showed that the two differed by a single pair of genes. Such genetic determinants act by affecting the rates of critical metabolic processes.

2. Nutrient supply and toxicity. As shown in the previous section, the growth of populations is limited by these factors. The same is true of the growth of a single cell or a single multicellular organism. Any environmental condition that affects either factor can also affect size and form.

3. The ratio of surface to volume. Imagine an organism perfectly spherical in shape, which starts life with a radius of 1 centimeter and grows to a radius of 10. Being spherical, its volume would be $\frac{4}{3}\pi r^3$ and its surface $4\pi r^2$. At the beginning, the volume would have totaled $\frac{4}{3} \times 3.14 \times (1)^3 = \frac{4}{3} \times 3.14 \times 1 = 4.2$ cubic centimeters (cm^3). After the growth period, the volume would be $\frac{4}{3} \times 3.14 \times (10)^3 = \frac{4}{3} \times 3.14 \times 1000$, or 4200 cm^3. Thus, the volume of the organism would have increased by $4200/4.2 = 1000$ times. The surface at the beginning would have been $4 \times 3.14 \times (1)^2$, or 12.56 square centimeters (cm^2), and at the end $4 \times 3.14 \times (10)^2 = 4 \times 3.14 \times 100$, or 1256 cm^2. Thus, its surface would have increased by $1256/12.56$, or only 100 times. In other words, when an organism increases in size, the volume increases much faster than its available surface area. The point of this is that if an organism experiences a thousandfold increase in protoplasmic volume, it is going to require a thousandfold more food to sustain itself and it is going to have to get rid of a thousandfold more waste products. But food enters and wastes leave through the surface of this organism which, as we have seen, increases much less than its volume. Consequently, the size the organism can attain is limited. Different species have overcome this limitation by:

1. Changing their shape in order to decrease the disparity between volume and surface as the two increase during growth.
2. Using their food supply more efficiently or by developing ways to make its entrance more rapid.
3. Using biochemical tricks for cutting down on the production of toxic wastes or by speeding the exit of wastes out of the system.

Many attempts have been made to describe mathematically the growth of a population of cells or of multicellular individuals. It is not difficult to arrive at an equation that can generate an S-shaped curve. What is difficult is to invest the constants of this equation with biological meaning, that is, to interpret them as being due to specific physiological mechanisms that initiate, maintain, and terminate growth. Generally, we start with the growth-affecting processes we know about (production of diffusible subunits, production of toxic wastes, exhaustion of the nutrient supply), then describe them in mathematical terms, and derive the proper equation relating the number or mass of organisms to the passage of time. The extent to which the equation (called the logistic equation) accurately describes growth, as measured in specific organisms, tells how much we really know about growth processes. The extent to which it does not, tells us how much is not known but, more important, provides a testing ground for the inclusion of additional physiological processes that we suspect may affect growth. The following paragraphs contain in abbreviated form the arguments that led to the derivation of the logistic equation. It is not expected that you will understand the subject completely from this exposition, but I hope you will appreciate from it that a rigorous, quantitative approach to biological pheromena is possible and represents a fertile field of investigation for the mathematically minded student.

The first part of the S-shaped curve, the period of so-called exponential growth, is simple to derive. It is described by the equation:

$$\log \frac{N}{N_0} = kt \qquad \textbf{1}$$

where N is the number of organisms at time t, N_0 is the starting number, k is a constant, and t is time. As mentioned previously, the growth of a population of cells that divide by binary fission follows the series 1, 2, 4, 8, 16, . . . and these can be stated as powers of 2, i.e., 2^0, 2^1, 2^2, 2^3, . . . in which the exponents refer to the number of generations of growth that have occurred. Therefore, starting with one cell and after n generations of growth, the number of cells would be 2^n. If we started with 1000 cells instead of 1, the series would be 1000, 2000, 4000, . . . i.e., 1000×2^0, 1000×2^1, 1000×2^2, . . . and after n generations, $N_0 2^n$, where N_0 is the starting number. The general statement of the number N of organisms would be:

$$N = N_0 2^n \qquad \textbf{2}$$

Let us assume that these cells reproduce once every two hours (a constant generation time). Then the population would have undergone one generation of growth in 2 hours, two in 4 hours, three in 6 hours, and so on. In short, the number of generations would be proportional to time, and this is stated algebraically as $n = k't$ where k' is a constant. Equation 2 can be restated as:

$$N = N_0 2^{k't} \qquad \text{or} \frac{N}{N_0} = 2^{k't} \qquad\qquad\qquad 3$$

Taking logarithms of both sides, we get:

$$\log \frac{N}{N_0} = (\log 2)k't$$

and if we make $(\log 2)k'$ equal to a new constant, k, the equation becomes:

$$\log \frac{N}{N_0} = kt \qquad\qquad\qquad 4$$

which is identical with equation 1. Remember that the only two assumptions used to derive this relationship are that 1 organism gives rise to 2 and that the generation time is constant. Obviously, the shorter the generation time, the faster the population would grow and the higher the value of k would be. Suppose the cells do not divide by binary fission but, instead, each cell gives rise to 3. Then the growth would be 1, 3, 9, 27, 81, . . . a series in powers of 3, and the equation would become:

$$\log \frac{N}{N_0} = (\log 3)k't$$

Only the value of k in equation 4 would change, but the basic equation would remain the same. In other words, whether 1 organism gives rise to 2 or 3 or more, or whether 2 organisms must cooperate to yield 3 or 4 or more does not change the equation, only the value of the constant.

But equation 4 as written does not describe the entire growth sequence. Note that as time passes (t gets larger), N/N_0 would get larger and never reach a limit, i.e., growth would never stop. To show how an automatic brake can be added to this equation, we derive it in another and more general way. Consider that growing organisms display two properties:

a. To get any progeny at all, you must start with at least one individual or, in the case of higher animals, with at least two of the right sexes (i.e., there is no spontaneous generation of life).

b. The more parents you have, the more progeny you will get. In other words, the rate of increase in the number of organisms is proportional to the number already present.

Now rate of increase is simply the change in the number of organisms per unit time, or:

$$\frac{\text{total change in number of organisms}}{\text{total change in time}}$$

We symbolize this as $\Delta N/\Delta t$. Since the rate of increase is proportional to the number, N, of organisms already present, we can write:

$$\frac{\Delta N}{\Delta t} = kN \qquad\qquad 5$$

This equation can be solved by the integral calculus. That is, the relation between N and t can be deduced from the way in which N changes with time. By these means (the mechanical manipulations are unimportant here), we obtain the same equation as already has been derived, i.e., equation 4.

Equation 5 can be elaborated to account for the stoppage of growth. To make it faithfully describe a real growth curve, we want to have the rate of growth start out high, giving us the first part of the growth curve, and then to decline steadily to zero, at which point the number of organisms would remain stationary. For some organisms that do not remain stationary after cessation of growth but actually die out, we would want the rate of growth to become negative after a time (a negative rate of increase is itself a decrease). These qualifications are accomplished by making k not a constant but a variable. For example, one way of doing this is to set k equal to $(a - bN)$, where a and b are constants. Equation 5 would then become:

$$\frac{\Delta N}{\Delta t} = (a - bN)N \qquad\qquad 6$$

At the start, when the number of organisms was very small, bN would be negligible, and the rate of growth would be substantially equal to $(a)N$ (i.e., would be like equation 5) and would yield the first part of the S-shaped curve. As growth proceeded and N became larger, bN would become larger and begin to detract appreciably from a. Thus the rate of growth would progressively decrease. When N became so large that bN equalled a, the term $(a - bN)$ would be zero, the rate of growth would be zero, and growth would cease. The constant b could be used to describe the decrease in the food supply or accumulation of toxic wastes that inhibit growth. In the case of the growth of organisms that serve as prey for other organisms, b could be used to describe the way in which the predator cuts down the growth of the prey (by killing off potential parents). In this case, b would not be a constant but would depend on the number of predatory organisms. Finally, b might be used to account for epidemics that kill substantial numbers of organisms and would be treated in much the same way as if a predator were feeding on the population. If we were studying the growth of an organ, say the number of liver cells in a human being, b might also be used to describe the action of hormones from other parts of the body upon the liver cells. The constant a has the same meaning as the constant k in the simpler equation 4; that is, it describes the generation time, the number of progeny, etc.

The Development
of Microorganisms

C H A P T E R   F O U R

As mentioned in Chapter 1, when we speak of developmental phenomena we mean an orderly, controlled succession of morphological and biochemical changes within an organism, the sum total of which constitutes its life cycle. We now deal with the developmental cycles of four microbial species, chosen because they illustrate four different facets of development:

1. Common Baker's yeast, *Saccharomyces cerevisiae*. This organism has a life cycle that includes cell growth and division (i.e., vegetative growth), the segregation of diploid cells to yield haploid gametes, and the fusion of gametes to yield diploid zygotes. These are the same features that make up the life cycles of higher forms of life including man. But in yeast cells, these activities occur in a relatively straightforward manner stripped of morphogenetic complications.

2. The water mold *Blastocladiella emersonii*. In these organisms we see the beginnings of cellular differentiation corresponding, in a superficial way at least, to what is observed in higher forms. Cells can develop along one of two mutually

exclusive pathways and the choice is governed by environmental conditions. For a short time after the choice is made, a cell can still back up and elect the alternate pathway, but ultimately a point of no return is reached and the choice becomes irrevocable, i.e., independent of further environmental shifts.

3. The alga *Acetabularia mediterranea*. In this organism the capacity of a cell for morphogenesis is raised to remarkable level of complexity. Certain convenient features make it possible to ask to what extent the morphogenetic pattern depends on a continual supply of instructions emanating from the nucleus and to what extent it can operate in the absence of such signals.

4. The cellular slime mold *Dictyostelium discoideum*. As long as they are growing, the individual cells of this organism remain independent of one another, but once growth ceases, they come together to construct an organized, multicellular entity composed of specialized, differentiated cells. Thus, this species encompasses the basic characters of microbial life on the one hand and metazoan and metaphytic life on the other.

THE LIFE CYCLE OF A TYPICAL UNICELLULAR ORGANISM—YEAST

We choose common Baker's yeast, *Saccharomyces cerevisiae,* to exempify the life cycle of simple microorganisms because it displays three features that are present in the cycles of most organisms within these groups:

1. The single cell as the unit of existence: In contrast to higher plants and animals (i.e., organized assemblies of specialized cells that are dependent on one another for their collective existence), the single yeast cell is the total organism.

2. Growth by vegetative (asexual) reproduction: Yeast cells multiply asexually, a single cell giving rise to two by budding. Sexual fusion of gametes does occur under special conditions (see below) but its occurrence is not obligatory to growth.

3. Sexual reproduction: You will recall from your study of genetics that the higher plant or animal, consisting mostly of diploid cells (two of each kind of chromosome), contains a few haploid germ cells or gametes (one of each kind of chromosome). Two haploid gametes of the appropriate sexes can come together and fuse to yield a new diploid organism.

This process is called sexual fusion and serves a very important function. The diploid individual receives a set of chromosomes from each parent. By meiosis, it in turn produces gametes with a single chromosomal set which, by random assortment, is generally made up of a mixture of chromosomes from each of the original parents. Thus, the genes of the parents are shuffled together in the offspring and are reshuffled in the gametes produced by that offspring (Fig. 4-1). Sexual fusion, then, is a source of genetic recombination, producing new varieties by reshuffling the old. New varieties are important to a population, for they ensure that there will always be types that can take advantage of new environments and thereby make the species fit to survive under a variety of conditions.

To clarify this point, consider a population of yeast cells living in a moderately cool bit of dirt and plentifully supplied with glucose to grow on. With the coming of summer, the soil becomes hot and the glucose is replaced by a different sugar, galactose. Now suppose that the population had originally consisted of two types: cells that were resistant to heat but could grow only on glucose, and cells that were sensitive to heat but could grow equally well on galactose or glucose. Under the new conditions, type A could stand the heat but not the new sugar; type B could grow on the new sugar but could not stand the heat. Of course, type A might produce a mutant that could grow on galactose and type B a mutant that could resist heat, but these would be exceedingly rare events that might not come to pass, in which case the yeast population would be wiped out. But if sexual reproduction could occur, the chromosomes bearing the genes for heat resistance and the ability to grow on galactose would be shuffled together in the zygote, and the recombinant type would be able to survive. Figure 4-1 illustrates this process.

Microorganisms such as yeasts and molds, protozoa, algae, and some bacteria are capable of sexual fusion. That is, diploid cells can by meiosis produce haploid gametes. These can be of different sexes (or mating types, as they are called). Haploid gametes of the appropriate sexes can fuse to yield new diploid individuals.

In higher animals, reproduction is tied to the sexual fusion of gametes. Human beings cannot bud or fragment. They must mate to reproduce their kind. In yeast cells, as in other microorganisms, sexual fusion is separate from reproduction. Yeast reproduce by asexual means, but under special conditions do employ sexual fusion to produce genetic recombinations (i.e., new varieties).

The life cycle of yeast is illustrated schematically in Fig. 4-2. The diploid individual is an elliptical cell. It reproduces asexually by budding and can do so indefinitely as long as it is supplied with nutrient materials and given physical conditions that permit growth. Under adverse conditions (when starved and unable to bud), the diploid cell undergoes meiosis to produce four haploid individuals. These are surrounded by thick walls and are resistant to drying, heat, ultraviolet radiation, etc. They are called *ascospores* and are contained within a large sac, or ascus. The ascus bursts; the ascospores are released and then germinate, yielding small

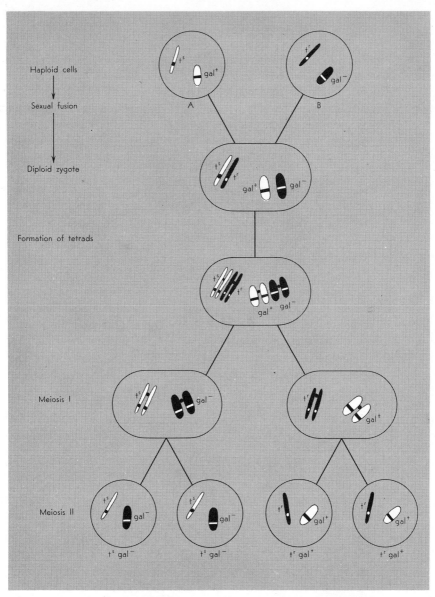

Fig. 4-1. Genetic recombination through sexual fusion. The gene for temperature sensitivity is indicated by the symbol t^s; t^r is its allele and denotes temperature resistance. We use gal+ to denote ability to utilize galactose, gal− to denote inability. Thus, cell A is heat sensitive and can utilize galactose; cell B is heat resistant but cannot utilize galactose. The chromosomes bearing these genes are shuffled together when cell A and cell B fuse to form the zygote. Each pair of chromosomes then duplicates to yield a quartet, or tetrad. The nucleus then divides twice (meiosis I and II), and in the process reduces the quartets to pairs and the pairs to singles. The random assortment of chromosomes during meiosis I can produce a situation in which the same cell will receive both the gene for temperature resistance and the gene for galactose utilization; that is, a recombination of the parental traits will take place.

round yeast cells, still haploid. Two haploid cells of the proper sexes can come together and fuse once again to yield a large diploid individual. The cycle is complete at this point and can be repeated.

Many questions come to mind. For example, what specific environmental conditions induce a diploid cell to undergo meiosis and produce ascospores? What causes the ascospores to germinate into haploid cells? What happens when the haploid cells are kept separate and not allowed to meet other haploid gametes of the correct sexual type? Can they grow by budding just like diploid cells? How is it that the haploid gametes can be of different sexes and yet look alike? What is the physiological basis of sex in these organisms? How is sex inherited in yeast? Some of these questions have been answered through research. Many still remain unanswered.

Fig. 4-2. The life cycle of yeast.

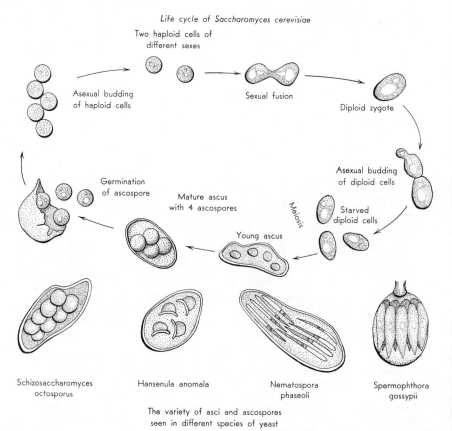

Life cycle of Saccharomyces cerevisiae

Two haploid cells of different sexes

Asexual budding of haploid cells

Sexual fusion

Diploid zygote

Asexual budding of diploid cells

Germination of ascospore

Mature ascus with 4 ascospores

Meiosis

Starved diploid cells

Young ascus

Schizosaccharomyces octosporus

Hansenula anomala

Nematospora phaseoli

Spermophthora gossypii

The variety of asci and ascospores seen in different species of yeast

BLASTOCLADIELLA EMERSONII

The life cycle of the water mold *Blastocladiella emersonii* is summarized schematically in Table 4-1. Tiny, flagellated swarm spores are released from the mature structure, swim about for a time, and then settle down to a sessile existence. The flagellum is resorbed or lost, the cell increases rapidly in size, and ultimately forms a two-celled structure, which is roughly spherical in shape and supported by a root-like hold-fast. At this point, one of two mutually exclusive pathways of development can be taken to yield either an *ordinary colorless sporangium* (OC) or a pigmented, thick-walled, *resistant sporangium* (RS). As Table 4-1 indicates, the difference between these two structures is not trivial but encompasses a multiplicity of biochemical as well as structural disparities.

Table 4-1

METABOLIC DIFFERENCES BETWEEN THE OC
AND RS FORMS OF *B. EMERSONII*

RS	Metabolic activity	OC
++	melanin	−
++	carotenoids	−
++	polyphenol oxidase	−
±	α-ketoglutaric dehydrogenase	++
±	succinic dehydrogenase	++
++	isocitric dehydrogenase	−
++	isocitritase	−
±	chitinase	++
++	glycine-alanine transaminase	±
−	cytochrome oxidase	++
±	respiratory activity	++
±	free amino acid pool	++

(++ = high activity or concentration; + = moderate; ± = barely detectable; − = absent.)

The choice of developmental pathways is apparently dictated by the concentration of CO_2 in the atmosphere. In the presence of a high concentration of CO_2, all the plants develop into RS; with a low CO_2 concentration, all become OC. The entire cycle, from swarm cell germination to the appearance of the mature structures, takes about 108 hours. If the organisms are incubated initially in a low CO_2 concentration (which eventually would lead to OC development) and then shifted after a few hours to a high CO_2 atmosphere, they can still change direction and become RS plants. But if the initial incubation in low CO_2 lasts longer than 20 hours, then the plants become irrevocably committed to OC development and a subsequent shift to high CO_2 has no effect. This has been called the *point of no return*. There is also such a point in RS development. Thus, if plants are incubated in high CO_2 (which would lead to RS development) for periods up to 50 hours and then shifted to low CO_2, they can still change direction and become OC. But after 50 hours they become committed to RS development irrevocably and subsequent shifts to low CO_2 are ineffective.

The enzymatic basis of the CO_2 effect and the mechanisms that establish these points of no return are currently being studied. There is no question but that such metabolic control systems are central to the problem of development. It should be noted that this type of phenomenon is frequently observed in differentiating cells of higher organisms. That is to say, the progress of a cell along a particular pathway of cellular differentiation may require special conditions in its local environment for a given period of time. But once past that period, such a cell becomes committed, i.e., it no longer requires the special environmental stimulus and despite its absence will develop along the dictated pathway.

THE LIFE CYCLE OF *ACETABULARIA*

Acetabulariae are green algae that live in temperate and subtropical marine waters. As shown in Fig. 4-3, the cell consists of (a) a large cap with

Fig. 4-3. Life cycle of Acetabularia mediterranea. **(After Brachet,** Biochemical Cytology, **p. 303.) In the laboratory, unlike nature, development of the adult structure from the zygote is direct, without regression, and takes only a few months.**

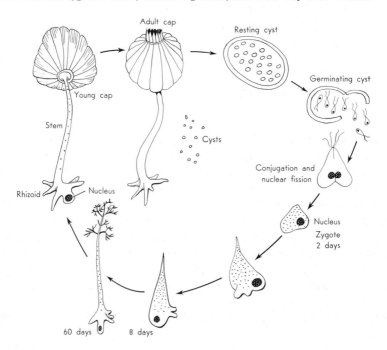

leaf-like members arranged like the petals of a daisy, (b) a long stalk, and (c) a root-like process at the bottom called the rhizoid. The stalk can be 4–6 cm long and the cap up to 1 cm in diameter in a mature individual. The growing cell contains a single, enormous nucleus usually situated in the rhizoid but sometimes found in the lower stalk.

In its natural habitat the complete life cycle of *Acetabularia mediterranea* takes about 3 years. After one year of growth the cell consists of a rhizoid, which has sent out rootlets that hold the alga fast to the substratum, and a cylindrical stalk without a cap. In the autumn, the stalk withers and falls off, leaving the rhizoid which subsists on stored food reserves through the winter. The following spring a stalk grows out and forms a rudimentary cap before regressing once more. In the third year a fully-formed stalk and cap appear. At this time the huge diploid nucleus undergoes repeated divisions to yield a great number of tiny nuclei that stream away from the rhizoid into the cap where they are gathered into large bodies with thick walls called cysts. The cysts are eventually shed from the cap and lie dormant. By this time, each of the nuclei (now haploid) within the cysts is surrounded by cytoplasm and a cell membrane. These miniature cells look like flagellate protozoa, being pear-shaped with two large flagella protruding from the front end. Eventually the lid of the cyst flips off, freeing the flagellate cells, which swim about for a time and then conjugate in pairs. The two cells become one, the two haploid nuclei fuse to yield a diploid one, and the zygote can then give rise after 3 years to an adult alga with cap, stalk, and rhizoid to complete the cycle.

In nature, *Acetabularia* can regenerate lost parts. For example, the seasonal disappearance of the stalk is followed by the synthesis of a new stalk, and the loss of the adult cap by mechanical abrasion is followed by the formation of a new cap. The regenerative powers of *Acetabularia* have been employed to study its morphogenesis and in particular the role played by the nucleus in morphogenetic processes. You can ask whether or not the nucleus has to be present at all for regeneration to occur. It can in fact be shown that pieces of stalk lacking a nucleus (anucleate) can produce new cell membranes, chloroplasts, a perfectly normal new cap, and, in a few cases, even a new rhizoid—in short, everything but another nucleus. After a few months all these parts die. In contrast, pieces containing a nucleus can regenerate lost parts over and over again. These activities are accompanied by extensive synthesis of proteins and nucleic acids. Thus, we can conclude that an anucleate segment of *Acetabularia* has stored reserves of material and energy sufficient to construct a complete adult at least once. To do so again and again, however, requires a continual supply of energy and materials, and for this, the nucleus must be present.

You can also ask whether the ability of a segment to form a new cap depends on the size or position of the segment. It turns out that long anucleate pieces of stalk can construct caps better, faster, and more frequently than short pieces, and pieces of stalk removed from near the cap have greater competence than pieces of equal length taken from positions near the rhizoid.

The various species of *Acetabularia* display wide differences in the form of the cap (number, shape, and size of the leaves, etc.). This specificity—i.e., the power to control cap design—appears to reside in the nucleus. Grafts have been made between two species, *Acetabularia mediterranea* (med) and *A. crenulata* (cren). The following results, which are also summarized in Fig. 4-4, have been obtained:

1. A rhizoid containing a nucleus (med) was joined to an anucleate segment of stalk (cren). After a few months of incubation a new cap was formed. Its appearance was intermediate between med and cren. If, however, the newly formed cap were cut off, a second cap was produced and

Fig. 4-4. Regeneration in Acetabularia. **Experiment 1 shows that a piece of one species, containing a nucleus, when joined to a piece of another species, without a nucleus, at first forms an intermediate cap, but, in subsequent regenerations, forms a cap characteristic of the species that contributed the nucleus. Experiment 2 shows that two nucleated pieces not only form an intermediate cap at first but also in subsequent regenerations. Experiment 3 shows that when two pieces of one species are joined to a piece of the other species, all containing nuclei, the cap is intermediate but resembles more closely the species that contributed the two nuclei.**

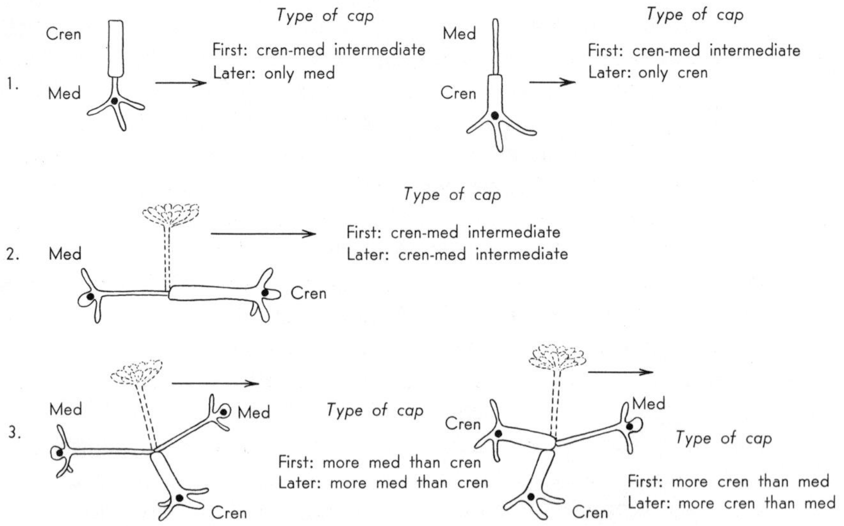

this was a med-type cap with no remnant of cren characteristics. Furthermore, additional removals of the cap yielded only med-type caps. The reverse experiment (cren rhizoid with nucleus and a med anucleate stalk segment) also yielded at first a cap which was intermediate between the cren and med types. When this cap was removed, all subsequently formed caps were purely cren.

2. Two nucleate rhizoids, one of each species, were joined, cut end to cut end. At the junction a stalk grew out which formed a cap intermediate between med and cren. Any subsequent removals of the cap yielded regenerates still intermediate between the two species.

3. Two nucleate rhizoids of cren were joined, cut end to cut end. The cut end of a third nucleate rhizoid (med) was fused to the junction point of the first two. A stalk grew out from this point whose cap was intermediate in appearance but much more like cren then med. When the experiment was reversed, i.e., the two med rhizoids joined with one cren rhizoid, the cap was much more like med than cren.

From these experiments we conclude that it is the nucleus which ultimately controls the morphogenetic activities of *Acetabularia,* presumably by directing the synthesis of substances that play specific roles in the construction of the cap. These materials are to some extent stored within the anucleate portions of the stalk but are not spread equally throughout. Thus, pieces of stalk taken from the apex have more of them than pieces taken from the base; longer stalk pieces have more of them than shorter pieces.

With these experiments as a background, it now is possible to inquire into the nature of the biochemical reactions that mediate morphogenesis in *Acetabularia* and into how the nucleus exerts control over them. Such problems represent an exciting challenge to young biologists and may lead to understanding of morphogenetic events in many organisms.

THE CELLULAR SLIME MOLDS

Living organisms are generally classified as unicellular (the individual is a single cell) or multicellular (the individual is an organized collection of specialized cells). Although such categories imply rigid distinctions, we must remember that discrete boundaries do not exist in nature but only in the minds of biologists. In reality, there is a middle ground occupied by organisms that are neither wholly unicellular nor wholly multicellular. For example, many protozoa, algae, fungi, and bacteria are transiently colonial; they come together for a time as loose clusters of quasi-independent cells with no organization or specialization. Others attain a primitive

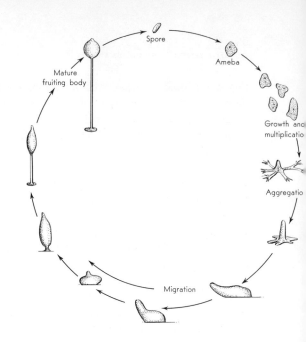

Fig. 4-5. The life cycle of Dictyostelium discoideum.

level of organization in which some cells of the colony become specialized
for feeding, others for sexual reproduction, etc. A highly complicated level
of organization is attained by the cellular slime molds.

Figure 4-5 summarizes the life cycle of one species called *Dictyostelium
discoideum*. The cycle is divided into four stages: growth, aggregation,
migration, and fruiting-body construction. It starts with the germination
of spores to yield ameboid cells. The amebae live in soil or on the agar
surface of a Petri dish, feed upon bacteria, and reproduce by binary fission.
When the supply of bacteria is exhausted, the cells stop growing and enter
the aggregation stage. The amebae stream radially toward central collecting points, and, as they reach the center, a conical mound of cells is
built up. When all the cells have aggregated, each conical mound falls
over on its side and is transformed into a worm-like slug up to a few
millimeters in length. The slug migrates over the surface and finally
comes to rest. It then proceeds to construct a fruiting body with a round
mass of spores at the top, a stalk enclosed in a cellulose sheath below,
and a basal disc at the bottom. These constitute three clearly different
cell groups. Ultimately the spores are cast off to repeat the cycle while the
stalk cells and basal disc cells desiccate and die. Figure 4-6 shows photographs of an aggregation sequence, migrating slugs, and the construction
of a fruiting body.

Fig. 4-6. **Slime mold morphogenesis. Left, an aggregation sequence (M. Sussman).
Top right, migrating slugs. (From J. T. Bonner,** The Cellular Slime Molds. **Princeton: Princeton University Press, 1959, Plate II.) Bottom right, the stages of fruiting
body construction—the photographs were taken approximately 1½ hours apart.
(Also from Bonner, Plate III.)**

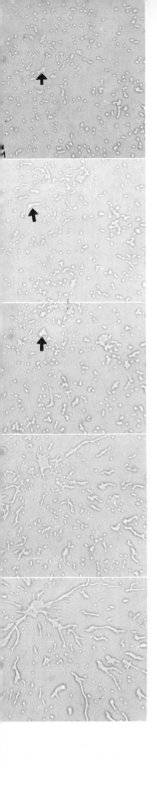

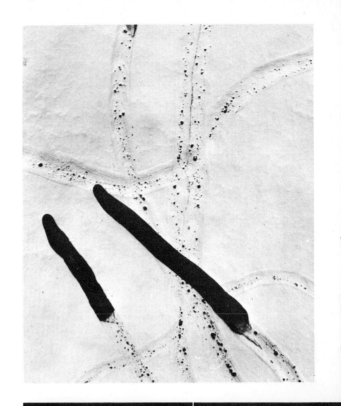

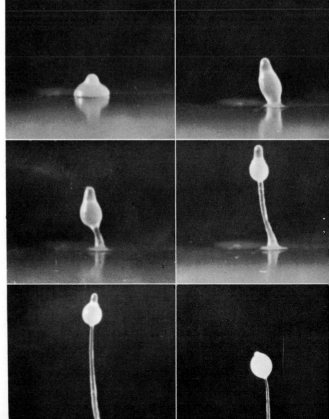

Cellular Differentiation

As we have mentioned, the fruiting body consists of three distinct cell groups: spores, stalk cells, and basal disc cells. These have different sizes, shapes, constitutions, and functions—as do the various tissue cells of a frog embryo. We can ask: What determines whether any given cell in the assembly will become a spore, a stalk cell, or a basal disc cell? This appears to depend on the order in which it entered the aggregate (Fig. 4-7). Cells that enter the aggregate first become the leading element of the migrating slug and ultimately the lower stalk of the fruit. Later arrivals

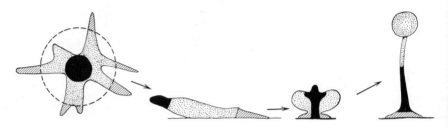

Fig. 4-7. The fate of the cells depends on the order in which they enter the aggregate.

take up progressively more posterior positions in the slug and become upper stalk cells and spores. Those entering last constitute the tail end of the slug and ultimately the basal disc of the fruit. One can tentatively imagine that the position of a cell in the aggregate and in the slug subjects it to a specific set of environmental conditions and of chemical signals imposed by its neighbors that forces it to become a spore or stalk cell or basal disc cell. These differences are reversible, at least up to the slug stage. Slugs have been cut into head and tail segments. Both could construct fruits separately. Although not completely normal, both contained all three types of cell even though the head segment would ordinarily have given rise to stalk only, while the tail segment would have yielded spores and basal disc cells but not stalk.

The complicated geometric relationships described above are not, however, the only ones capable of resulting in the appearance of spores and stalk cells. A mutant strain of *D. discoideum* forms only flat, amorphous aggregates that develop no further. Yet, as shown in Fig. 4-8, normal-looking spores are found in these aggregates along with short, randomly oriented sections of stalk sheathed in cellulose and containing stalk cells. Furthermore, this chaotic organization is accompanied by the appearance

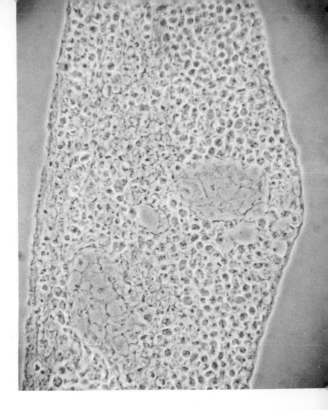

Fig. 4-8. A thin section cut through an aggregate formed by the mutant. Spores are mixed in a chaotic array with short sections of stalk containing the usual vacuolated cells.

of many biochemical end products found in the mature fruiting bodies of the normal strain. These include several kinds of polysaccharide, certain other macromolecules, pigment, etc. Thus, cellular differentiation in the slime molds is not uniquely dependent on a certain kind of cellular organization or geometric form. As you will see in Chapter 6 the same is true for the developing cells of vertebrate embryos.

You can also ask whether any cell at any stage of the morphogenetic sequence *can give rise to progeny* capable of producing normal fruiting bodies. To answer the question, cells from aggregates, slugs, and immature fruiting bodies have been dispersed and grown separately. The colonies derived from each could, without exception, aggregate and form normal fruiting bodies with viable spores. In the mature fruiting bodies it is impossible to free most of the stalk cells from their cellulose sheath but at least some cells coming from this region, if collected early enough, live and yield progeny that can make complete fruiting bodies. Thus, when a cell engages in fruit construction its genetic constitution remains intact, i.e., it can pass on to its descendants the ability to produce complete, normal fruiting bodies.

Cell differences can be observed even during aggregation. Thus, under proper circumstances we can demonstrate that some cells have a great capacity to affect their neighbors in such a way as to initiate centers of aggregation (such as the one seen in Fig. 4-6) whereas others have very little initiative capacity. Specialization is also apparent in the migrating slugs. Thus, if the front end (about 10 per cent of the cells) is separated from the rear, the former continues to migrate while the latter stops in its tracks. If the front end is replaced, the two parts fuse and migration of the whole slug proceeds once again in normal fashion. This suggests that two "cell types" are present—leader cells and follower cells—and that the behavior of the slug results from the organized interaction of the two. Finally, we can observe the differentiated synthesis of special biochemical products, such as polysaccharides and other substances mentioned above. These products arise at particular stages of the morphogenetic sequence, some of them being confined to special locations in the fruiting body.

The details described above suggest the following conclusions:

1. The aggregate, slug, and fruiting body are organized entities in which different cells do different things both biochemically and morphologically in order to complete the organization of the whole.

2. These specialized activities are not caused by nor do they lead to changes in the genetic material of the cell. Furthermore, at least up to the slug stage, a cell fated to engage in one kind of activity, can by a change in position be made to engage in another.

3. The underlying biochemical activities are subject to rather strict control with respect to time and place of occurrence.

Cell Interactions During Development

The development of a multicellular system is accompanied, indeed is largely directed, by a hierarchy of cell interactions. One cell or one tissue may stimulate or inhibit the development of another by exchange of appropriate chemical agents. It is this matrix of interactions that ensures the harmonious organization of the whole, i.e., that the components will develop at the right time, in the right place, and in the right amount. As we will see in Chapter 7, the use of cell interactions reaches its highest degree of complexity and refinement in vertebrate embryos. However, the beginnings of these control mechanisms operate in primitive organisms such as the slime molds.

A case in point is the way in which the cells aggregate. A large body of evidence has been accumulated to show that outlying cells are attracted and caused to aggregate by specific chemical agents produced at the center. (Attraction of cells by a chemical compound is called *chemotaxis*.) For example, if the amebae are permitted to aggregate under a flowing stream of water (see Fig. 4-9), a center forms, but the cells upstream are unaffected. Only those downstream are attracted by and move toward the center. This is just what you would expect if the center were produc-

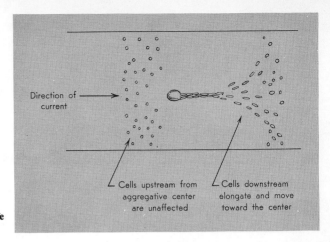

Fig. 4-9. Myxamebae aggregate under a flowing stream.

Direction of current

Cells upstream from aggregative center are unaffected

Cells downstream elongate and move toward the center

ing some chemical agent that was being carried downstream by the water current.

Regulation

The term regulation refers to the ability of a morphogenetic system to turn out normal products of different absolute sizes. For example, individual frog embryos or tadpoles or adult frogs of a given species can vary markedly in size and yet be perfectly proportioned. That is, the sizes of the various parts (arms, legs, head, etc.) at each developmental stage bear precise relationships to the total length or total mass. Furthermore, if cells are surgically removed from a very young frog embryo, the remainder will develop into a very tiny but nonetheless normal tadpole, again demonstrating the same relationship of parts to whole.

Slime molds also display regulatory capacities. For example, myxamebae packed together in a solid mass produce relatively large migrating slugs and fruiting bodies; some are as much as 5 mm in length and contain hundreds of thousands of cells. If sparsely distributed, the myxamebae form tiny slugs and fruits a few tenths of a millimeter in length that contain a few hundred cells. Yet the gross proportions and the relative amounts of cells comprising the various parts of the fruiting body remain the same. This regulatory capacity is exhibited at a truly startling level by a mutant of *Dictyostelium discoideum* that can form normal fruits containing hundreds of thousands of cells or as little as 10 to 12 cells. Figure 4-10 shows an example of the latter, a fruiting body with 12 cells —9 spores, 2 stalk cells, and 1 basal disc cell. This exquisite miniature contains all the elements of a morphogenetic system—cellular differentiation, cell interactions, and regulation—but in a tiny packet of cells.

Mutant Strains

A large number of mutants have been isolated that display aberrant morphogenetic capacities. Some of these can form fruiting bodies with

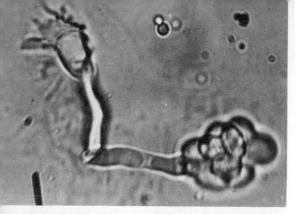

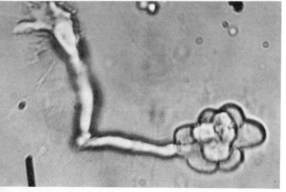

Fig. 4-10. Two views of a fruiting body formed by the "fruity" mutant of D. discoideum. This highly organized multicellular structure consists of 9 spores, 2 stalk cells, and 1 basal cell.

viable spores but with fruits whose shapes and sizes are greatly different from those of the parent strains; such mutants are given names like fruity, curly, glassy, and forked. Other mutants are *morphogenetically deficient,* i.e., they cannot complete the normal morphogenetic sequence; instead they stop at various stages along the way. Thus, some cannot aggregate at all and remain as separate cells; others aggregate but cannot develop any further.

Résumé

In summary, these are some of the lessons learned thus far from the study of slime molds:

1. Just as in the development of higher forms (vertebrate embryos, etc.), slime-mold development involves the appearance of new cell types that play a causal role in the construction of the multicellular whole. We would like to know how and when they arise and in what numbers, and what physiological mechanisms are responsible for the roles they play in morphogenesis.

2. Here, as in other developmental systems, a matrix of cellular interactions helps to regulate the process. Chemical signals are passed during aggregation, and during migration of the slug. Finally, chemical signals tell some cells to become spores, others to become stalk cells, and still others to become basal disc cells in the fruiting body. We want to know what are these signals and how they act.

3. Normal development need not involve participation of huge numbers of cells. Instead, even as few as 10 cells can provide the components and the chemical interactions needed to construct a perfect fruiting body.

The Development
of a Primitive
Animal:
The Coelenterates

A *tissue* can be defined as a group of cells having similar structure and function and arranged in a compact, organized array. Thus, we talk of connective tissue or bone tissue or epidermal tissue. The evolutionary transformation of multicellular organisms from quasi-amorphous conglomerates of cells into structures with well-defined tissues was a significant step, for it enabled these tissues subsequently to combine into organs and organ systems and thus permitted the levels of complexity that higher animals have since attained.

The most primitive group of organisms extant that displays a definite tissue organization is the Phylum *Coelenterata* (or *Cnidaria* as it is now called). This is a group of fresh-water and marine animals that includes *Hydra* (a favorite laboratory animal in elementary biology) and its relations—the sea anemones that abound on rocky coasts, the corals, the jellyfish, and the awesome Portuguese Man of War, whose toxin has paralyzed many unwary swimmers and led to death by drowning. A brief résumé of the general properties of these organisms illustrates their primitive condition:

47

1. The body is composed of only two tissues, the outer epidermis and the inner gastrodermis. These arise early in the development of the coelenterate embryo. In contrast, the tissues of all higher animals stem originally from three embryonic cell layers. Within the two coelenterate tissue layers are a number of cell types, some of which appear in Fig. 5-1.

2. The body is essentially in the shape of a sack. That is, only one opening exists, and this serves as both mouth and anus. The internal lining of the sack (gastrodermis) serves to digest the food carried in through the mouth, but there is no suggestion of a digestive organ system.

3. There is no blood or circulatory system, no excretory or respiratory organs.

4. There is a diffuse network of nerve cells, but no central nervous system and only rudimentary sense organelles.

The adult coelenterates occur in two forms. One is the *polyp,* which has a tubular body with a closed end that is attached to the substratum. There it grows singly or in colonies. The second is the *medusa,* a free-swimming, gelatinous body with a shape like an umbrella; its mouth hangs down from the concave undersurface. Figure 5-2 shows examples of these. They are variants of the same basic sack-like structure. In the polyp, the sack (coelenteron) is elongated and narrow with its open end up. In the medusa, the sack is squat and rounded with its open end down. Some species appear both as polyps and medusae during their life cycles. In other species, one or the other adult form may be rudimentary and very short-lived or entirely absent.

In both forms, the mouth is surrounded by tentacles, which contain special stinging cells called *cnidoblasts* (hence the name *Cnidaria*). Upon stimulation, they shoot out spear-like processes bearing powerful toxins

Fig. 5-1. Cell types found in coelenterates.

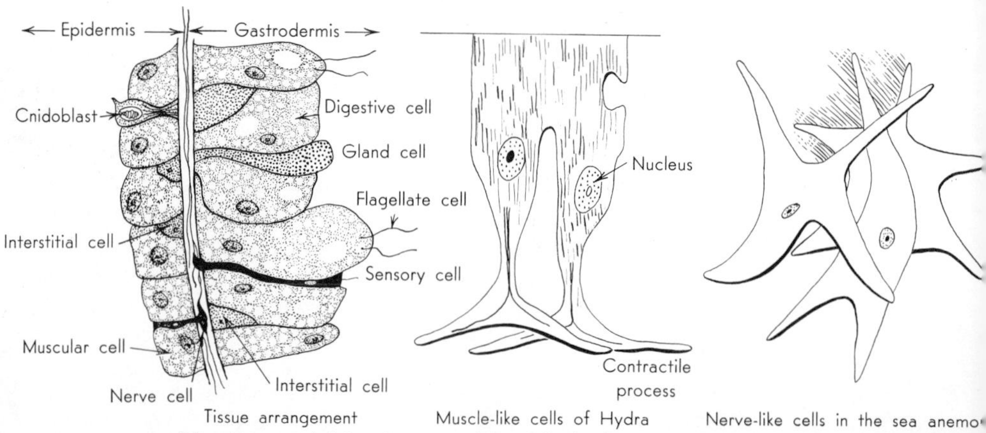

Tissue arrangement
(after Storer and Usinger)

Muscle-like cells of Hydra
(after Schechter)

Nerve-like cells in the sea anemone
(after Schechter)

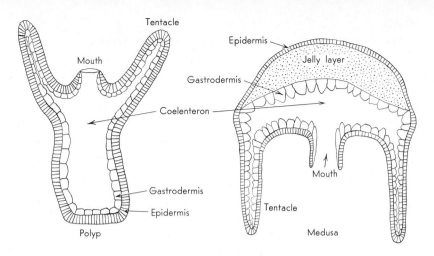

Fig. 5-2. Body plans of adult coelenterates.

to paralyze their prey (small crustaceans, insect larvae). Very little is known about the toxins. The few that have been studied appear to be proteins. When injected into rabbits, they damage nerves and elicit the formation of antibodies, as do certain snake venoms, tetanus toxin from bacteria, and other poisonous proteins.

LIFE CYCLE OF THE GENUS OBELIA

Both polypoid and medusoid stages figure prominently in the life cycle of *Obelia,* which is summarized in Fig. 5-3. The polyps grow as colonies upon rocks and shells in shallow marine waters. The colony is fastened to the substratum by a mass of root-like runners that bear slender, branched stems, and from these extend polyps of two kinds: the feeding polyps equipped with mouth and tentacles, and the reproductive polyps, which lack all feeding mechanisms and are designed for one purpose—to produce medusae that bud off from the central cylinder and escape through the hole in the vase-shaped outer covering.

The roots and stems of the colony are hollow cylinders composed of the same two tissue layers, epidermis and gastrodermis. The internal space, called the *coelenteron,* is filled with fluid, is continuous, and extends into the polyps. This means that the feeding and reproductive polyps and the cells in the walls of runners and stems are all in intimate contact, and all parts of the colony can be supplied with the food materials that enter through the feeding polyps.

Both kinds of polyp are initiated as buds on the stems. At first the bud is simply a protuberance of the stem wall that contains both tissue layers. The protuberance lengthens rapidly by cell division and by migration of cells from other areas. Infoldings and constrictions of the tissue

49

ultimately give rise to the organs that are characteristic of the feeding and reproductive polyps.

As we have mentioned, the medusae also are formed by budding from the central cylinder of the reproductive polyps. Fully formed, they are minute jellyfish, shaped like an umbrella and rimmed with tentacles. The mouth hangs down from the concave side and leads upward into the digestive cavity in the middle of the umbrella. They move by jet propulsion, water being forced out of the mouth, and feed upon crustacea and protozoa. They are of two sexes, male and female. Their gonads develop inside the digestive cavity, and eggs or sperm are propelled through the mouth. Fertilization takes place in the sea.

The fertilized egg promptly cleaves into two, the two into four, and so on until a hollow ball of cells is produced. This is called the blastula stage and corresponds to a similar stage in the development of vertebrate embryos (see Chapter 6). Some of the cells are forced into the interior of the ball to become the gastrodermis, while the cells that remain outside become the epidermis. This corresponds to the gastrula stage of embryogenesis, encountered in higher invertebrates and vertebrates, during which their three basic tissue layers appear. After tissue separation, the *Obelia* embryo elongates, and cilia appear over the outer surface. The constituent cells now begin to transform into sensory, gland, and muscle cells and cnidoblasts. At this point, embryogenesis is concluded, and the animal is called a *planula larva* (i.e., the immature, larval form of the adult polyp).

Fig. 5-3. The life cycle of Obelia. **(After Storer and Usinger.)**

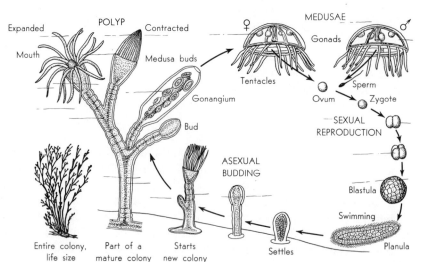

The *planula* swims about for a period of hours to days and then attaches to a rock or shell. The attached end develops into a root-like runner, and the free end acquires a mouth and tentacles. Buds appear, the polyp colony is initiated, and the cycle is complete.

POLYMORPHISM IN THE COELENTERATES

Polymorphism (a variety of forms) occurs at two levels in the coelenterates. First, there is the basic difference in the adult structures (i.e., polyp and medusa). You may ask why it is that in an *Obelia* colony a bud on the stem of a feeding polyp gives rise to another polyp, whereas a bud on the cylinder of a reproductive polyp gives rise to a medusa. Are the constituent cells different, or is it merely that they inhabit different areas of the colony and so are subject to different environmental conditions? Actually the same sort of question can be asked about our own bodies: Namely, why is it that the cells in one part of a human embryo develop into brain cells and in another part develop into liver cells? These questions will be taken up in detail in the chapters on cellular differentiation.

The second level of polymorphism is exemplified in *Obelia* by the specialization of the polyps. Another genus, *Hydractinia,* displays an even greater range of differences in polyp structure, as Fig. 5-4 shows. *Hydractinia* colonies live on the surface of a specific type of snail shell but only when those shells are inhabited by hermit crabs. Three types of polyp develop:

1. Feeding polyps. These correspond in essential features to the feeding polyps of *Obelia.*

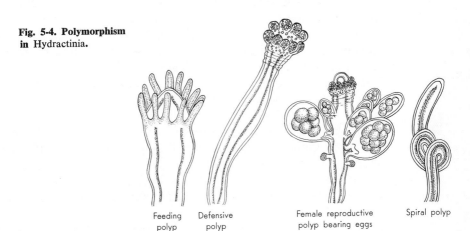

Fig. 5-4. Polymorphism in Hydractinia.

Feeding   Defensive   Female reproductive   Spiral polyp
polyp   polyp   polyp bearing eggs

2. *Defensive polyps.* These are concentrated at the lip of the snail shell. They lack a mouth and their tentacles are reduced to small knobs arranged in two circular rows. The stems have considerable musculature and can whip about fiercely, thereby permitting the cnidoblasts on the tentacle knobs to discharge a concentrated volley upon contact with the foe. Spiral polyps may be variants of these.

3. *Reproductive polyps.* In *Hydractinia,* the medusa stage is absent. Instead, the reproductive polyps produce sex cells directly. There are two sexes (a single colony produces reproductive polyps of one sex only) and the male and female varieties are quite differently formed.

REGENERATION OF POLYPS AND MEDUSAE

The decapitation of a polyp is followed within a few days by the appearance at the cut end of a new head complete with mouth and tentacles. If a segment is cut from a polyp stem or from a root-like runner and incubated in water, the isolated piece can give rise to a new polyp. Similarly, a piece taken from a medusa, if large enough, can reorganize itself into a complete functional medusa with all parts normal and intact.

The regeneration is specific. That is, a piece of tissue taken from a polyp regenerates a polyp. A piece taken from a medusa regenerates a medusa. In a recent study, it has been shown that this specificity extends even to the kind of polyp from which the piece of tissue was taken. Cut stems taken from a *Hydractinia* colony regenerated true to type: Stems of feeding polyps regenerated only feeding polyps; those from reproductive polyps regenerated only reproductive polyps. Two conclusions are permissible from these data:

1. A complete, functional, adult coelenterate contains many cell types (i.e., cnidoblasts, epidermal cells, gland cells, muscle cells, nerve cells, etc.). These results show that even a small piece of coelenterate tissue either contains all the necessary types or can give rise to them by appropriate transformation of one cell type to another.

2. The pieces of tissue appear to "know" from what kind of adult they came and to be able to reorganize themselves accordingly.

Compare these results and conclusions with those gained from the study of *Acetabularia* regeneration described in Chapter 4. Please note that they are essentially identical, save that in one case we deal with a structure whose parts are divided up into cellular packets, whereas in the other we deal with one whose parts are not so divided but are nevertheless organized in a specific manner.

Regeneration by stem segments has other interesting features that are summarized in Fig. 5-5. First, the rate and extent of the development of a new head depends on the part of the stem from which the segment is taken. If a polyp stem is cut into serial segments of equal size, the segment from the end nearest the previous head (distal end) develops a new one fastest and most completely, while that from the lowest (proximal) end is the most laggard. In other words, along the stem there is a gradient of potency for the production of new heads. In addition, one part of a stem in producing a new head can prevent another part from so doing. For example, a stem segment of moderate length develops a new head at

Fig. 5-5. Regeneration of polyps by stem segments.

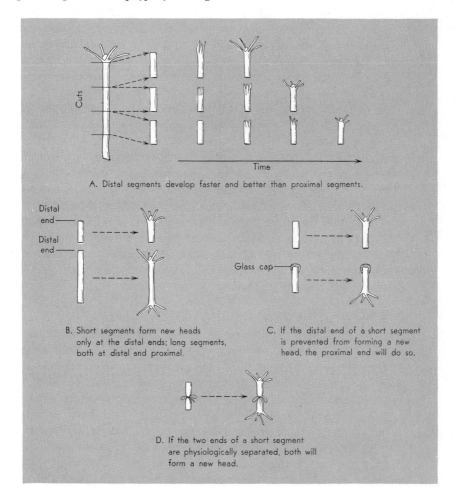

A. Distal segments develop faster and better than proximal segments.

B. Short segments form new heads only at the distal ends; long segments, both at distal and proximal.

C. If the distal end of a short segment is prevented from forming a new head, the proximal end will do so.

D. If the two ends of a short segment are physiologically separated, both will form a new head.

only one cut end, and this is invariably at the distal end. However, if we prevent the distal end from regenerating by slipping a glass cap over it, then the proximal end will form the head (although slower than the distal end would have done it). This interaction can be prevented in two ways: first, by making the stem segment so long that the two ends are not in close contact; second, by separating the two ends physiologically. The latter can be accomplished by tying a string tightly around the middle of the segment so as to prevent the flow of materials and cells between the ends. When these measures are taken, heads form at both ends without any evidence of competition between them.

This type of phenomenon is common in developmental systems. A case in point is the development of the hind limb in a chick embryo. As described in Chapter 6, the limb originates as a small protuberance from a specific point along the flank of the embryo. Areas surrounding this point can also be shown to be capable of forming the protuberance and ultimately a complete limb. We can ask, therefore, why the limb forms where it does and why other areas that have the potency for limb construction normally do not grow one.

A system in which may parts can develop in a certain way but only one part actually does so is called a *morphogenetic field,* which will be discussed in detail in the next section. The dominance of one part of the field over another maintains regularity of development. It ensures that a coelenterate polyp will have one head and that it will be where it ought to be, i.e., at the top of the stem. It ensures that a chicken will have one tail, two wings, and two hind limbs in the right places. Moreover, it makes for versatility, for if by accident the dominant area of a morphogenetic field is destroyed, a neighboring area has the potency to take its place. Thus, the top of the coelenterate stem and only the top normally forms a head. But if by accident the head is destroyed, a new one can be constructed from underlying tissues.

MORPHOGENETIC FIELDS

The concept of a morphogenetic field had its modern inception in the work of Professor C. M. Child, a famous American embryologist. Dr. Child was the first to emphasize the fact that in such fields one area will gain dominance over another by its superior capacity to form a given structure and by its ability to inhibit neighboring areas from doing so. He and his students provided many examples of field development in the regeneration of coelenterates, flatworms, and starfish, and in the formation of embryos. Thus, we speak of head fields, limb fields, tail fields, heart fields, etc., to denote this kind of development. Attempts have been made to describe morphogenetic fields in mathematical terms in an effort to understand the processes by which dominance is established. A simplified version of the mathematical argument is given below.

Consider a group of coelenterate stem cells that can form a head. We divide this group into two separate areas. How fast the stem cells in an area will construct a head should depend on their inherent capacity (i.e., developmental potential) to be converted into head cells and also on the number of cells available in the area for head construction. This can be written formally as:

$$\text{rate of head development} = (\text{developmental potential}) \times (\text{number of stem cells}) \qquad \mathbf{1}$$

The rate of development in area I might be greater than, equal to, or less than that of area II, depending on the relative developmental potential and on the numbers of cells that compose each area. A difference in developmental potency, however, is not enough to create a morphogenetic field, since, if the two areas were isolated from each other, each would construct a head at its characteristic rate and neither would dominate the other. It is necessary for the two areas to be able to interact with one another.

Suppose the developing head cells can pour out materials that inhibit others from becoming head cells. First of all, the cells in area I that had already been incorporated into the developing head would inhibit the remaining stem cells in that area from changing into head cells. The degree of inhibition would depend on the inherent sensitivity of the area I stem cells to being inhibited by their own head (autosensitivity) and on the number of head cells that are producing the inhibitory materials. This inhibition would have to be subtracted from the rate of head development defined in state 1. Thus,

$$\begin{pmatrix} \text{rate of head} \\ \text{development} \\ \text{in area I} \end{pmatrix} = \begin{pmatrix} \text{developmental} \\ \text{potential} \\ \text{of area I} \end{pmatrix} \times \begin{pmatrix} \text{number of} \\ \text{stem cells} \\ \text{in area I} \end{pmatrix} - \begin{pmatrix} \text{auto-} \\ \text{sensitivity} \\ \text{in area I} \end{pmatrix} \times \begin{pmatrix} \text{number of} \\ \text{head cells} \\ \text{in area I} \end{pmatrix} \qquad \mathbf{2}$$

According to this statement, the rate of development would be very high at the beginning of head formation. Then, as the head grew larger and more and more cells were incorporated into it, they would produce inhibitory materials and detract materially from the rate at which additional stem cells would be incorporated into the head. Meanwhile, the number of stem cells would decrease as they were converted into head, and the first term on the right side of the above equation would decrease. Eventually, the two terms on the right side would cancel out, and the rate of head development would become zero (i.e., the head would now be complete). In the case under consideration, the rate would fall to zero before all the stem cells had been converted into head cells—after all, a coelenterate head would look pretty silly without a stem to support it.

Now suppose the two areas are in contact with each other (for example, if the two have a common coelenteron and are bathed by the same body fluid). Then the head cells of area II would inhibit the stem cells in area I in the same fashion as described above. That is, the rate of area I development will be impeded by the inherent sensitivity of area I stem cells to the inhibitory products * of area II head cells (*heterosensitivity*) and by the number of head cells in area II. The complete description of the rate of head development in area I would then become:

$$
\begin{array}{l}
\begin{pmatrix} \text{rate of head} \\ \text{development} \\ \text{in area I} \end{pmatrix} =
\begin{pmatrix} \text{developmental} \\ \text{potential} \\ \text{in area I} \end{pmatrix} \times
\begin{pmatrix} \text{number of} \\ \text{stem cells} \\ \text{in area I} \end{pmatrix} -
\begin{pmatrix} \text{autosensi-} \\ \text{tivity in} \\ \text{in area I} \end{pmatrix} \\[2em]
\qquad \times
\begin{pmatrix} \text{number of} \\ \text{head cells} \\ \text{in area I} \end{pmatrix} -
\begin{pmatrix} \text{heterosen-} \\ \text{sitivity} \\ \text{in area I} \end{pmatrix} \times
\begin{pmatrix} \text{number of} \\ \text{head cells} \\ \text{in area II} \end{pmatrix}
\end{array}
$$

$$3$$

The same sort of equation can be written for the rate of head development in area II.

We can now ask how area I can gain dominance over area II and prevent it from forming a head. This can be done in a number of ways:

1. Area I could have a much higher developmental potential or a much greater number of cells. In either case, it would form a head so fast and begin pouring out inhibitory materials so soon that area II wouldn't have a chance to get started.

2. Area I might be very resistant to auto-inhibition (i.e., the inhibitory materials might be carried away by the body fluid circulation quickly, whereas area II might be very sensitive (i.e., the inhibitory materials might not be carried away).

3. Area I might not be very heterosensitive, while area II might be extremely so.

4. Even were developmental potentials, sensitivities, and cell num-

---

* I have described the interaction between areas I and II as the result of the production of inhibitory materials. We could equally well account for it by assuming that the areas compete for a common pool of nutritive materials that serve to stimulate development. Were this the case, area II would inhibit area I by depriving it of these materials and vice versa. Actually, the mathematical argument turns out to be the same whether we put it in terms of inhibition or deprivation.

bers equal, area I could gain dominance by starting head formation first. The head start (forgive me) would permit it to inhibit area II.

Any one of these conditions, or a combination of them, would serve to establish the dominance of area I.

At present, none of the biochemical and genetic mechanisms that create differences in developmental potential or that exert inhibitory effects have yet been identified for any morphogenetic field. Thus, this kind of developmental study is in its infancy.

The Development
of the
Vertebrate Embryo

The purpose of *embryogenesis* is to create a young, function-ing, multicellular organism. The raw materials are (1) an egg, a single cell, large with respect to sperm but tiny with respect to the finished product that is to come, and (2) a sperm containing little more than a nucleus that, when joined with the egg nucleus, will provide the instructions needed to produce the embryo. The problems of embryogenesis are solved by the following strategems:

1. Cleavage: The fertilized egg is first subdivided into a large number of smaller cells, because little self-contained packets are easier to control and alter than a single, undi-vided mass of protoplasm.

2. Gastrulation: The cleaved cells move about so as to create three basic tissue layers. These become further sub-divided and give rise to the tissues and organs of the func-tional adult.

3. Organ formation: Each subdivision of the three orig-inal tissue layers becomes a semi-autonomous system within which cells appear by division, are grouped into tissues, and finally become functional entities (kidney, spleen, brain, etc.). Thus, many changes occur simultaneously within the subsystems of the developing embryo, and they must be linked in such a way as to operate harmoniously, in the right place at the right time. This is accomplished in part by having chemical signals pass between developing subsystems so that one of them can trigger or curtail the next and therefore provide chronological order to what would otherwise be chaos.

In the rest of this chapter we shall consider, in some detail, these processes, as well as the earlier phases of embryogenesis, i.e., the formation and union of the gametes.

THE EARLY STAGES OF EMBRYOGENESIS

The Formation of Gametes: The Sperm

The first step for young men in the recipe for a successful marriage is: find a girl. Similarly, nature's instructions to a sperm are: first, find your egg. To accomplish this, the mature sperm is a stripped-down model equipped with organs of locomotion and with a high rate of metabolism so that it can generate energy to move rapidly over relatively great distances. Once in contact with an egg, it must deliver a nucleus containing a haploid set of chromosomes, one-half the complement of the future embryo. Figure 6-1 is a drawing of the sperm of several animals and

Fig. 6-1. Spermatozoa.

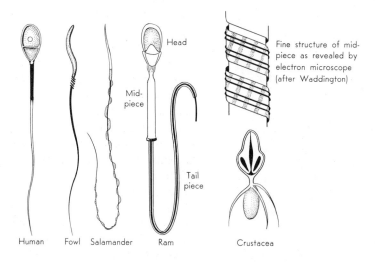

Head

Fine structure of midpiece as revealed by electron microscope (after Waddington)

Midpiece

Tailpiece

Human   Fowl   Salamander   Ram   Crustacea

includes a reconstruction of what we see in an electron microscope when we look at the midpiece of ram sperm. This should give you some idea of the sperm's structural complexity. Various sperm may look very different, but they all contain these basic parts:

1. The head. This portion is taken up almost completely by the sperm nucleus.

2. The midpiece. This part contains material that will be put to use after the sperm penetrates the egg. It aids in the fusion of the egg and sperm nuclei and in the cleavage of the fertilized egg into the first two daughter cells.

3. The tail. This can be long or short, flexible or stiff. It may vibrate, whip, or rotate in a screw-like motion depending on the species. It is the locomotor organelle.

Fig. 6-2. Maturation of the sperm.

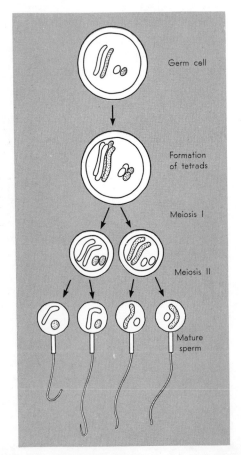

The ancestors of the sperm start out as ordinary diploid individuals. The germ cells, as they are called (both in males and females), arise early in the development of the embryo. They appear to be irreplaceable, because when embryos are treated in a manner that destroys or removes (by ultraviolet irradiation or surgery) the germ cells, the resultant adult organisms are sterile.

Gametogenesis, the process by which the diploid germ cells give rise to haploid sperm or eggs, is properly within the domains of cytology and genetics but will be reviewed briefly here. Figures 6-2 and 6-3 are schematic summaries of the maturation of male and female gametes. For simplicity, let's imagine that the diploid nucleus contains only two pairs of chromosomes. Each chromosome duplicates, yielding a quartet, or tetrad, of chromatids. The cell itself then divides into two, each with a pair of sister chromatids. This is *meiosis I.* These cells in turn divide without chromosomal duplication to yield four

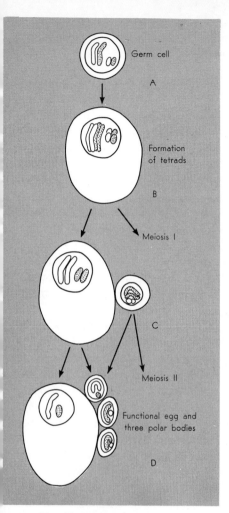

Germ cell

A

Formation
of tetrads

B

Meiosis I

C

Meiosis II

Functional egg and
three polar bodies

D

Fig. 6-3. Maturation of the egg.

(*meiosis II*) so that the daughter nuclei end up with two chromosomes rather than the original four and are therefore haploid. In the case of sperm, the daughter cells are changed from ordinary-looking cells into functional gametes after meiosis II.

The Formation of Gametes: The Egg

The egg has three functions to perform:

1. To supply a nucleus containing half the chromosomal complement of the future embryo.

2. To supply almost all the cyptoplasm upon union with the sperm.

3. To supply food reserves that will enable the embryo to develop to a stage where it can begin to feed upon exogenous materials.

Because it must do all these things, the animal egg is a cell of giant size. Consider for example, the size of a hen's egg. Even that of the mammal, .05–.25 mm, is considerably larger than ordinary body cells.

The egg is covered by a protective envelope: in birds, by an inorganic shell; in amphibians, by a jelly coat made up of polysaccharide and protein of high molecular weight. In mammals, a single layer of very small protective cells cover the egg surface. The egg proper is bounded by one or more membranes. A single haploid nucleus resides within, together with cytoplasmic constitutents whose fine structure, revealed by the electron microscope, does not seem to be different in kind from the constituents of other cell types. Finally, there is yolk, the food supply for the embryo. This is a heterogeneous mixture of fat droplets, granules, and small bodies, bounded by membranes. Some of these are highly pigmented and, because the yolk is organized material, can be seen to occupy definite regions of the egg and to be parceled out amongst the daughter cells in a definite manner.

There are great differences among eggs of the animal species with respect to yolk content. For example, the eggs of marine animals contain relatively little yolk because the embryo begins active feeding at a very early stage. What yolk there is in marine eggs is distributed homogeneously and not concentrated in a particular region. In contrast, the eggs of birds contain enormous amounts of yolk. For example, the hen's egg contains a tiny disc of cytoplasm sitting on top of an enormous mass of yolk. Insect eggs also contain large amounts of yolk, which is situated at the center of the egg and surrounded by a thin outside layer of cytoplasm. In these forms, the embryo undergoes considerable developmental changes before emerging as an actively feeding organism; hence the large supply of food reserves. At the top of the evolutionary scale are the mammals. A mammalian embryo develops in a sense as a parasite inside its mother and receives a continuous supply of food materials from her through the circulatory system, much as if it were just another of her internal organs. A large yolk reserve is therefore unnecessary, and mammalian eggs resemble the primitive marine eggs in this respect.

The maturation of the egg, like that of the sperm, proceeds via two meiotic divisions from a small diploid parent cell (Fig. 6-3). The parent cell chromosomes duplicate, and the cell then grows to enormous size. The proteins, fats, nucleic acids, and carbohydrates that constitute the yolk are synthesized within the egg or are received from without (contributed by so-called "nurse" cells). When the final size is attained, the egg nucleus goes through meiosis I and two cells appear. The cell division is very unequal, however, and the lucky nucleus finds itself with most of the cytoplasm and yolk, the unlucky nucleus with very little. Meiosis II follows and now four haploid cells are present. Again, because of a very unequal division, one of the daughter cells contains virtually all the yolk and cytoplasm. This, then, is the mature egg, and its three tiny sisters (called polar bodies) shortly degenerate and disappear. Figure 6-3 is a schematic summary of the process.

In most cases, developing eggs reach stage C and then lie dormant until fertilization, at which time the process is completed and the surviving female gamete nucleus unites with the sperm nucleus. In a few cases the egg is arrested at stage B and very few reach stage D before fertilization.

The Life Span of Gametes

A mature egg must be fertilized within a short time, if it is to be fertilized at all. Thus, human eggs generally remain functional for about 12–24 hours after their release from the ovary. The eggs of sea urchins, which are shed into the water, last for 48 hours, but the eggs of most invertebrates as well as fish and amphibia must be fertilized within a few minutes of being shed. The life spans of other animal eggs are of the same order of magnitude as those of human eggs.

Sperm are generally just as short-lived as eggs. However, in some cases (bees, bats) the sperm can remain viable for years within the female genital tract. The study of sperm preservation has recently gained great economic importance because of the use of artificial insemination for livestock breeding. In the case of cattle, a stud bull is induced to service an artificial vagina (a water-jacketed rubber tube with a collecting bottle at one end and the bull at the other). About 4.5 ml of semen is collected per ejaculation, and the bull can be used for service up to 10 times in a two-hour period. The semen is cooled slowly to a temperature just above freezing and can be stored for seven days at most. It is diluted before use and injected into the uterus of a cow in heat, through a pump. A good stud bull can be used to impregnate literally thousands of cows in a single season. It should also be noted that many human females fail to conceive by natural means even though the gametes of both husband and wife are perfectly viable. In such cases, artificial insemination of the wife with her mate's semen is generally successful in inducing pregnancy.

Fertilization

The act of fertilization can be divided arbitrarily into three phases: (1) penetration of the egg by the sperm, (2) activation of the egg, and (3) the union of egg and sperm nuclei.

PENETRATION. Contact between sperm and egg is generally the result of random collision. The discharge of huge numbers of sperm by the male increases the chance that at least one such collision will occur. Upon contact, the sperm is bound tightly to the outer surface of the egg. This is probably accomplished by chemical reactions between proteins concentrated at the surfaces of both gametes. Fertilizin, isolated from eggs, causes sperm to become sticky and to clump together, whereas antifertilizin obtained from the sperm does the same thing to eggs. The substances are specific and act only upon gametes of the same species. Thus, fertilizin and antifertilizin may increase the chance of an effective and lasting contact between egg and sperm. The evidence that the fertilizins actually do operate during fertilization is still equivocal, however.

The sperm that is now bound to the egg must penetrate its membrane. Material extracted from sperm has been shown capable of dissolving the egg membrane by enzymatic action. Presumably the intact sperm employs the enzyme to dissolve a hole big enough to permit entrance. In mammals, the egg is surrounded by a layer of tiny follicle cells cemented together by a substance called hyaluronic acid. Mammalian semen contains an enzyme, hyaluronidase, that dissolves this cement and permits the sperm to slip through. Many pathogenic bacteria use this same device to slip through body tissues and invade all parts of the organism.

ACTIVATION. As mentioned previously, the egg as it develops in the female stops at one or another stage of meiosis and lies dormant until activated by contact with the sperm. Certain characteristic changes may then occur:

1. Completion of meiosis. The nuclear membrane breaks down and the egg nucleus completes the meiotic process (where it is incomplete).

2. Fertilization cone. In some eggs a conical projection pushes up through the surface jelly from the egg membrane. It "captures" the sperm at the jelly surface and by contraction draws it down toward the egg. Meanwhile, the sperm dissolves a portion of the membrane to permit ingress.

3. Block to polyspermy. Penetration by the first sperm makes most eggs almost instantaneously impervious to the entrance of any others. The mechanism of this reaction is still unclear. In a few species, however (some reptiles and insects), the entrance of more than one sperm (poly-spermy) is a normal event. One of the sperm nuclei fuses with the egg nucleus and the others degenerate and disappear.

4. Rearrangement in egg contents and physiology. Upon fertilization the egg changes its shape, generally veering toward the spherical, the per-meability of the egg membrane to salts and other substances rises mark-edly, cyptoplasmic materials migrate to new areas, and the axes of the future embryo (dorsal-ventral, anterior-posterior) are fixed.

Many eggs can be activated in the absence of sperm. Among treat-ments found successful are: X-ray and ultraviolet irradiation, introduction of foreign protein by a needle, heat shock, and addition of certain salts and acids. The activated egg proceeds through the changes noted above and goes on to cleave and construct an embryo. The eggs of certain organisms (sea urchins, starfish, frogs, bony fishes) can develop perfectly normally without fertilization by sperm and give rise to viable adults. The process, called *parthenogenesis,* is carried out routinely in nature by colonial insects including bees. Although only the egg nucleus is present, the cells of a parthenogenetic embryo need not remain haploid. In some cases the activated haploid egg duplicates its chromosomes without cell division, thereby producing a diploid, homozygous individual.

FUSION OF NUCLEI. The sperm head and midpiece enter the egg, mem-branes disappear, and the sperm chromosomes arrange themselves on a spindle constructed by material in the midpiece (Fig. 6-4). Sperm and egg nuclei migrate toward each other and the egg chromosomes arrange themselves on the spindle. The pattern now resembles that seen in meta-phase of mitosis. The chromosomes duplicate, the first cleavage of cells occurs, and two daughter cells, now diploid, emerge. The egg has become an embryo.

Fig. 6-4. Fertilization. (After Wilson.) (1) Sperm contacts egg. (2) Sperm head and midpiece enter egg through fertilization cone; egg nucleus proceeds through meiosis II. (3) Sperm nucleus enlarges; midpiece constructs spindle and asters; meiosis II of egg completes to yield polar body and functional, haploid egg nucleus. (4) Sperm and egg nuclei migrate toward each other across midpiece spindle; nuclear membranes break down. (5) Chromosomes dispose themselves upon mitotic spindle. (6) Chromosomes duplicate and mitosis draws to a close in preparation for first cleavage.

CLEAVAGE

In all eggs, fertilization is followed by a period of extensive cell division without an increase in size. The fertilized egg is cleaved repeatedly into smaller and smaller cells. The early divisions are generally synchronous; thus the egg yields two cells, the two produce four, the four, eight, and so on. From this time on, synchrony may disappear and different parts of the embryo may cleave at different rates. At the end of the cleavage stage, the embryo, now called a *blastula,* is a ball of thousands of small cells (blastomeres).

Although there is no size increase during this period, a considerable amount of synthesis occurs. The cleavages are regular mitotic divisions so that chromosomes and total nuclear content must be duplicated in the daughter cells. This means extensive synthesis of deoxyribose nucleic acid plus other nuclear constituents. In addition, a great deal of ribose nucleic acid and proteins, including enzymes, are formed in the cytoplasm. The energy and raw materials for these processes come, of course, from the supply of yolk.

Cleavage performs at least three functions in embryonic development:

1. It provides an adequate number of cells, i.e., building blocks for the future organization of tissues and organs.

2. It lays the groundwork for the gross design of the embryo (dorsal-ventral axis, anterior-posterior axis, etc.) by shifting around the material (both cytoplasm and yolk) of the egg and compartmentalizing this material within separate cells.

3. It brings nuclear and cytoplasmic materials into balance. The egg starts as a cell with a single nucleus and an enormous amount of cytoplasm. During cleavage, total cytoplasmic content does not change markedly but thousands of nuclei appear as cell division proceeds.

The pattern of early cleavage is determined in large part by the amount of yolk in the egg. In eggs that contain a little yolk that is homogeneously distributed, cleavages are equal; that is, the daughter cells are always about the same size. Figure 6-5A shows this type of cleavage in *Amphioxus*. Eggs with a large amount of heterogeneously distributed yolk cleave unequally. Figure 6-5B illustrates this type of cleavage in the frog. The yolk in the frog egg is concentrated in one hemisphere (the vegetal), and decreases in a sharp gradient toward the opposite (animal) hemisphere. The first two cleavages split the frog egg longitudinally to produce four cells shaped like the segments of an orange. The third cleavage is transverse and separates the yolky (vegetal) part from the nonyolky (animal) part. The split is unequal, since the four animal blastomeres are much smaller than the four vegetal ones. Subsequently, the yolky cells cleave far more slowly than the nonyolky ones. The result is that in the completed blastula, the dorsal part contains many small cells while the ventral part contains fewer but larger cells. In fish and birds, the extreme of yolkiness is reached. The cytoplasm and nucleus of the egg sit atop a huge ball of inert yolk. The yolky area does not cleave at all and only the little cap on top divides into cells (Fig 6-5C).

The specific appearance of cleaving cells is much the same in all embryos. A groove (called the cleavage furrow) appears at one point of the egg. For example, in the frog the first furrow appears at the animal pole. The furrow then deepens and extends downward on both sides. The two ends meet at the vegetal pole. The furrow then extends inward radially, finally constricting the egg into two sister blastomeres.

In most cases, as the cells cleave, a cavity appears in the middle of the ball of cells. This is the *blastular cavity*. Thus, by the end of the cleavage stage, the embryo is a spherical or flattened hollow ball generally one cell thick. The blastomeres can vary in size, yolk content, and cytoplasmic organization, but no tissues and certainly no organs yet exist.

The early cleavages are regular phenomena that occur at specified times after fertilization. Thus in the egg of the frog, *Rana sylvatica,* incubated at 18°C, the first cleavage (longitudinal) occurs at 2.5 hours after ferti-

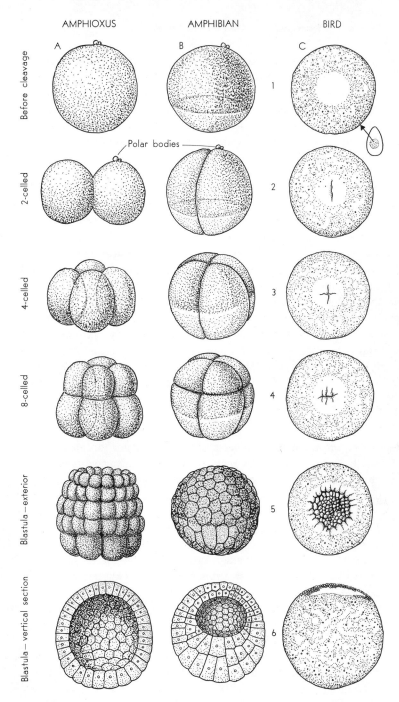

Fig. 6-5. Patterns of cleavage in Amphioxus, **frogs, and birds. (From Storer and Usinger.)**

lization, the second (also longitudinal) occurs at 3 hours, the third (transverse) at 4.5 hours, the fourth (again longitudinal) at 5.5 hours, leaving the embryo as a still solid ball consisting of two hemispheres of eight cells each, the dorsal being smaller than the ventral. The blastular cavity soon appears and produces a hollow ball with a thin roof and a thick floor. By 21 hours the blastula is complete and gastrulation commences.

GASTRULATION

At the beginning of gastrulation, the embryo is a hollow or solid ball of cells. By the end of gastrulation, the embryo consists of three basic tissue layers: an outer layer (*ectoderm*), an inner layer (*endoderm*), and an intermediate layer (*mesoderm*). Gastrulation, then, involves a series of integrated cell movements that lead to the formation of these discrete layers. Because the movements are quite complex, they are hard to follow. Investigators have observed them by time-lapse movie photography and by marking areas of the blastula with carbon particles or dyes and following the path of motion. In this way they have been able to map the origins of the three tissue layers back to cells of the early blastula stages. The gastrular movements of many species have now been studied; they show a variety of ways of establishing three tissue layers. Three mechanisms of gastrulation will be discussed: those in *Amphioxus,* in frogs, and in chickens.

Amphioxus

Amphioxus or the Lancelet is a primitive chordate, a marine animal resembling the fishes. As seen in Fig. 6-5A, cleavage is virtually equal and produces a blastula whose vegetal-pole cells are only slightly larger than those at the animal pole. Gastrulation begins when the cells at the vegetal pole move to the interior (Fig. 6-6). As they pass upward, the blastular cavity grows progressively smaller and finally disappears when the vegetal-hemisphere cells press up against the animal-hemisphere cells. The embryo is now a double-walled cup such as might be made if we pressed upon one side of a hollow rubber ball. The external wall is the ectoderm and will ultimately give rise to the epidermis, certain external organs, and the nervous system. The internal wall is the endoderm, and the hollow U-shaped cavity is called the *archenteron.* Surrounded by endodermal cells, it is the primitive digestive tract (gut). The embryo now lengthens and the site of the old animal pole becomes the anterior end of the embryo; the site of the old vegetal pole becomes the posterior.

Until now the gastrula has been only two-layered, but the third layer (mesoderm) appears at this time. Three long tubes of cells are pinched off from the endoderm. The middle one becomes the *notochord,* a flexible skeletal rod which persists in amphioxus as its axial supporting member. (In higher chordates, the notochord appears during embryogenesis but is later surrounded or replaced by the vertebral column.) The lateral tubes grow by cell division into large tissue masses that are divided into segments along the length of the embryo and are called *somites*. These expand and plaster themselves exteriorly up against the ectoderm to become the second layer of skin, and interiorly against the endoderm to become the outer lining of the gut. Eventually internal organs such as the gonads, kidneys, etc. will pinch off from the mesoderm and inhabit the internal

Fig. 6-6. Gastrulation and later embryonic stages as they occur in Amphioxus. **(After Villee.)**

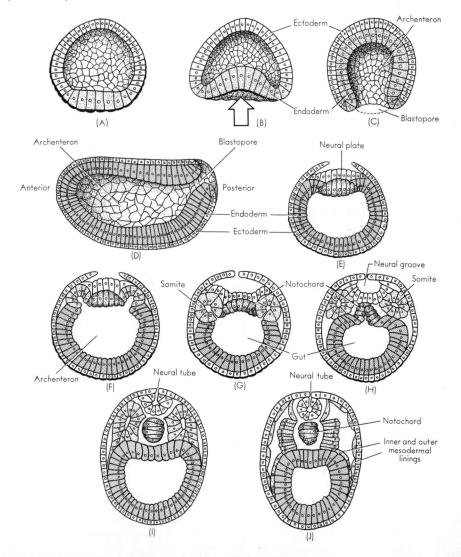

body cavity that lies between the mesodermal linings. With the formation of the third basal layer, the gastrula is complete.

The Frog

At the end of the cleavage stage, a frog embryo is a hollow ball with a thin roof and a thick floor. A small dimple appears near the vegetal pole when large yolky cells leave the surface of the egg and begin to press inward. This process of inward movement is called *invagination*. As more cells invaginate, the dimple becomes a crescent-shaped groove curving downward toward the vegetal pole. The groove is called the *blastopore* and has an upper (dorsal) and a lower (ventral) lip (Fig. 6-7).

The sheet of cells from the upper surface of the blastula moves downward and converges upon the blastopore. As the cells reach the dorsal lip, they turn inward and enter the interior of the embryo. Similarly, the ventral cells invaginate over the ventral lip of the blastopore. As the presumptive (future) mesoderm folds inward over the dorsal lip, it separates from the endoderm that entered before it. The mesoderm plasters itself against the outer layer of ectoderm and continues to move away from the blastopore and up toward the animal pole. The detached endodermal cells move to the middle of the embryo and form a long trough-shaped structure. The edges of the trough move up and around, finally meet, and the trough is converted into a tube. The mesoderm breaks up longitudinally into three masses: a central tube, the notochord (this later

Fig. 6-7. Gastrulation stages in the frog. (After Hamburger.)

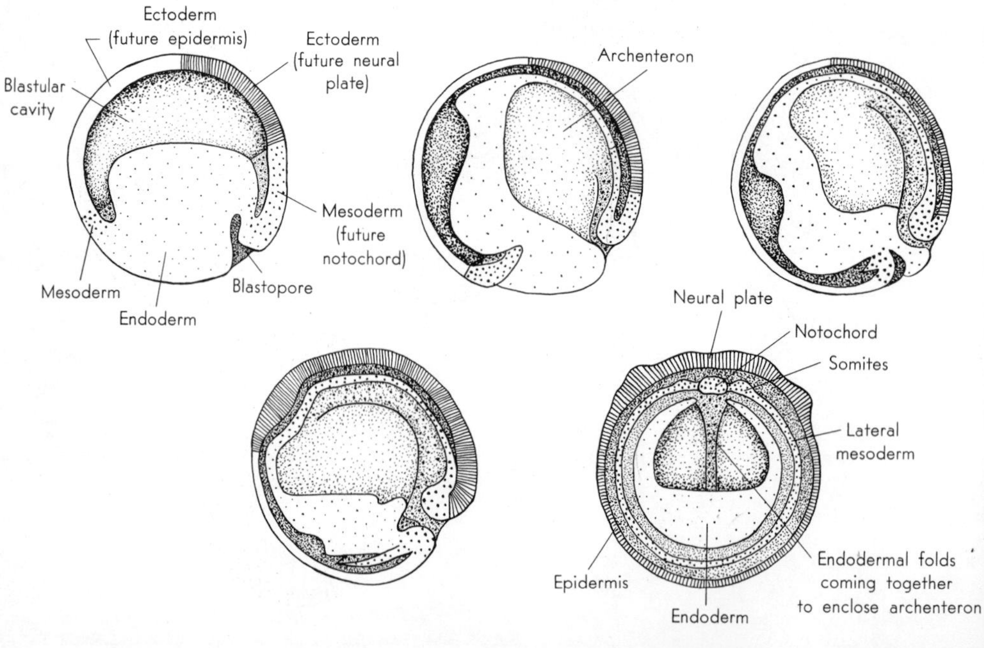

disappears and is replaced by the vertebral column), and two lateral masses that later segment and become somites.

The Chick

At the end of cleavage, a chick blastula is a small cap of cells several layers thick that sits on top of the yolk. A thin cavity appears within the blastoderm, so that at completion it is a flattened hollow ball. Despite a great deal of descriptive study, it is not clear whether the lower layer of cells simply splits off from the upper layer or whether cells at the edges of the cap move underneath it and join at the center to form the lower layer. In any case, the upper layer of cells is the source of both ectoderm and mesoderm; the lower layer is the endoderm.

A long narrow groove called the *primitive streak* appears on the surface of the blastodisc and runs from the approximate center back toward one edge. This edge will become the posterior of the embryo and its opposite will be the anterior. Cells stream toward the primitive streak and then turn under to spread out in a sheet between the ectoderm and the endoderm. This intermediate layer is mesoderm and when it is fully formed, gastrulation is complete. Note that the embryo is still only three isolated sheets of cells like a layer cake. Eventually the blastoderm in the anterior and posterior regions and at the sides will get tucked under the embryo. When the two infoldings meet in the middle, the ectoderm will have been transformed from a single sheet of cells into a complete outer covering. The endoderm will also have been tucked under to produce a long hollow tube, the gut. The mesoderm at the same time gives rise to notochord and somites. Figure 6-8 is a schematic representation of these changes.

The Subsequent Development
of Ectoderm, Mesoderm, and Endoderm

An embryo develops in one sense much as a delta-choked river travels to the sea. That is, it starts as one big channel and then splits up into several smaller ones that in turn branch and rebranch. The original embryonic channel is the fertilized egg. The three intermediate channels are ectoderm, mesoderm, and endoderm. Figure 6-9 summarizes these ramifications.

Most of the research carried out so far on gastrulation has been descriptive, consisting of efforts to follow the patterns of the cell movements, to trace the origins of the three basic tissue layers back into the blastula and even to the fertilized egg, and to account for the tissues and organs that are produced in the later embryonic stages. Now, biologists can begin to ask questions at the mechanistic level. For example, what is

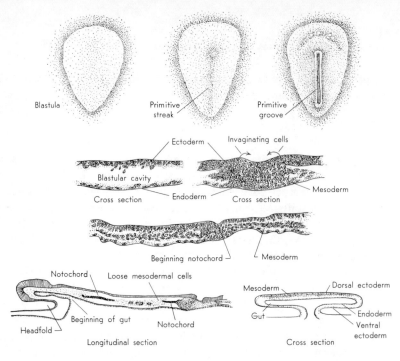

Fig. 6-8. Gastrulation in the chick.

Fig. 6-9. Channels of development of the vertebrate embryo.

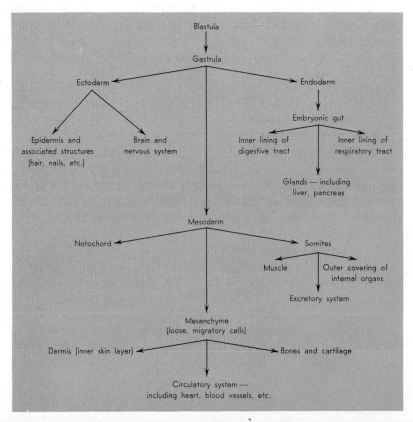

the motive force for gastrular movements? That is, are the cells pushed from behind or pulled from in front, or does each cell move as an individual at the same rate as its neighbors? Why is it that the cells move to specific areas of the embryo? What motivates somite cells to plaster themselves against ectoderm and endoderm respectively? By what mechanism do endoderm cells move up and around so as to produce a tube-like gut? Are these simply random movements that are channeled into specific patterns by the shape of the embryo, or are the cells attracted or repelled by specific chemical stimuli and then move toward or away from the places where these substances are produced?

As you can see, many problems of biological interest involving gastrulation still remain unsolved and are open to investigation.

ORGAN FORMATION

Development of the Central Nervous System

Toward the end of gastrulation, ectodermal cells immediately in front of the blastopore (or in front of the primitive streak of the chick and mammal) begin to divide rapidly. The resultant crowding forces some cells beneath the surface, and in this manner a thick plate of ectoderm appears. This is the *neural plate*. The wave of cell division proceeds anteriorly and the neural plate finally extends along the entire dorsal line of the embryo. Now the edges of the plate become elevated into folds and the center of the plate is depressed. This produces a groove which steadily deepens as the neural folds come together along the midline.

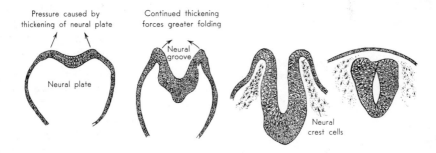

Fig. 6-10. Neural tube formation.

Finally the upper margins of the folds touch and fuse, and the groove is now formed into a tube, the neural tube, which is overlaid with a continuous layer of ectoderm. Figure 6-10 shows these foldings in cross section,

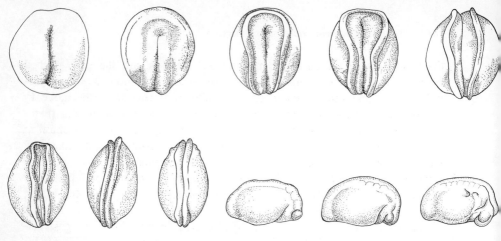

Fig. 6-11. Changes in the external form of the amphibian embryo, from the appearance of the neural fold to the completion of the neural tube. (After Hamburger.)

and Fig. 6-11 shows the external appearance. As described below, the neural tube is the rudiment of the central nervous system, including the brain and the spinal cord. The embryo has reached the neurula stage.

Originally the neural tube is wider at the front end of the embryo. This width is enhanced by local swellings that produce three distinct bulges. These are the forebrain, midbrain, and hindbrain. Now the forebrain bulges laterally and two cup-like rudimentary eyes appear. Simultaneously the surface ectoderm (the epidermis) folds inward to meet the optic cups. Folds are pinched off and ultimately develop into eye lenses. The ears and nostrils also appear at first as epidermal infoldings. Look at Fig. 6-12 for a schematic drawing of these developments. In the meantime the spinal cord undergoes considerable growth and cell division. Mesodermal cells migrate toward the cord and aggregate around it and around the underlying notochord. They transform into cartilage and ultimately into bone tissue, thus giving rise to a hollow vertebral column with associated ribs, and so forth.

The spinal-cord cells are at first large and rounded. They now assume typical neuron shapes, spinning out long fibers. The cells in the ventral part become motor neurons, and their fibers penetrate peripheral organs and tissues. Cells that had previously been crowded out of the neural folds (the neural crest cells in Fig. 6-10) migrate

Fig. 6-12. The development of the brain and associated sense organs. (After Waddington.)

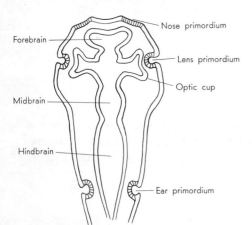

Forebrain

Nose primordium

Lens primordium

Optic cup

Midbrain

Hindbrain

Ear primordium

down toward the cord and aggregate into cell masses called *ganglia*. These cells become sensory neurons that send dendrites to connect up with the dorsal part of the spinal cord and send axons into surrounding tissues. In this manner the complete sensory-motor network is constructed.

The growth of the nerve fibers and their penetration into peripheral tissues is a fascinating subject. The process has been studied: (a) in the normally developing embryo, (b) by cutting functional nerves in order to follow the regeneration of a fiber from the old stump, and (c) by separating embryonic nerve cells and growing them in an artificial medium (usually on a blood clot surrounded by blood serum and other constituents found by experience to be delectable to a nerve cell). The body of the presumptive nerve cell appears to send out an ameboid process; the nucleus remains within the cell body. Protoplasm flows into the process causing it to move ahead while still connected to the cell body by a thin protoplasmic strand. This is the fiber. Special cells called Schwann cells then flatten out and wrap themselves around the fiber in much the same way that insulation is wrapped around an electrical conductor.

The first fibers to penetrate into surrounding tissues are called *pioneer fibers* and these are followed by others that apply themselves to the pioneer and form a cable. Many problems involving the mechanism of nerve growth remain unsolved. For example, how does a fiber know to what specific organ or tissue it must go, and how does it know when it has gotten there? How do the follower fibers duplicate the precise route of the pioneer fiber? Why do only fibers of similar function collect into cables? What control system ensures that certain tissues will receive many sensory and motor fibers while others will be innervated only sparsely?

Development of the Digestive and Respiratory System

While the neural system takes shape, other parts change as well. Externally, the embryo elongates and becomes sculptured into head and trunk regions. Limb buds, tail buds, and gill slits appear. Internally, the mesoderm splits into notochord and somites; the endoderm takes a long trough-like shape and rolls up into a tube, the primitive gut, which is open at the rear through the anus and later at the front through the mouth.

At first the gut is a simple tube stretching from mouth to anus. At the anterior end, five folds appear on each side that penetrate and finally pierce the mesoderm and make contact and fuse with the outer ectoderm. Slits appear where endoderm and ectoderm meet. These are the gill slits. In fish they remain as functional organs, but in higher vertebrates they disappear and the component tissues are transformed into other organs. The lungs also originate from the anterior gut, first as a simple outpocketing which soon branches into two bag-like structures.

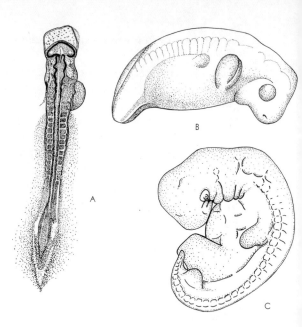

Fig. 6-13. Advanced embryos: (A) the chick, (B) the salamander, and (C) the human.

Similar pocketings, extensions, and local swellings in the posterior portion of the gut result in the formation of stomach, intestines, liver, etc.

Development of Mesodermal Structures

By the end of gastrulation, the mesoderm makes up the bulk of embryonic tissue. The notochord is the first mesodermal organ to appear, and the remainder of the mesoderm is spread out as a thin sheet lying between the ectoderm and endoderm. This sheet breaks up into longitudinal strips. The thick strips lying on both sides of the notochord become segmented into blocks of tissue called somites. The somite cells migrate toward the notochord and the spinal cord and form the vertebrae (as described previously) and also skeletal muscles. They also spread upward to underlie the outer ectoderm and become part of the skin and inward to become the outer covering of internal organs. Portions of the mesoderm lateral to the somites pinch off as longitudinal strips of tissue and give rise to the urogenital tract, including kidneys, gonads, etc. The heart and circulatory system also originate from the nonsomite mesoderm.

Development of Limbs

The limbs first appear as slight external swellings (limb buds) that rapidly elongate. The bud is simply a mass of loose mesodermal tissue capped by an ectodermal cover. As the limb elongates, the mesodermal cells grow rapidly in number and come together into a series of tight aggregates corresponding to the skeletal elements of the adult limb. They then are transformed into cartilage and finally into bone tissue. The remaining mesoderm forms muscles and blood vessels. Meanwhile, the external sculpturing of the limb, joints, digits, etc. is accomplished.

Cell Interactions
during Growth
and Morphogenesis

We have seen the complexities that attend the construction of a multicellular organism. Many new cell types arise and must maintain fairly rigid numerical proportions. Cells must migrate to specific areas of the aggregate and must be integrated into tissues and organs. All these processes involve a bewildering array of biochemical activities that must occur in strict chronological order.

How does the system maintain a balance of kind, number, place, and time? Obviously, each subunit of an organism cannot be permitted to develop autonomously, disregarding other subunits. Each, therefore, must receive information from other parts about what these have been doing in the immediate past and about what it may do and must not do in the immediate future. We will now concern ourselves with the exchange between cells of chemical messengers that trigger, assist, control, and inhibit developmental events.

"MANY CELLS DO WHAT FEW CANNOT DO"

The simplest example of this kind of interaction is seen in cultures of microorganisms or of dispersed animal or plant cells growing in a liquid nutrient medium, a topic taken up in detail in Chapter 3 and briefly reviewed here. Such cells, when inoculated into fresh medium, experience a lag of variable duration before they can begin to reproduce actively. The lag results in large part from the need of each cell to accumulate threshold concentrations of key compounds (vitamins, amino acids, etc.) before cell division can commence. Yet as fast as the cell produces these compounds, they pour out into the medium by diffusion through the cell membrane. As the external concentrations of these key substances rise, the rate of diffusion out of the cell decreases, enabling the internal concentrations to increase and finally reach the necessary thresholds. The time needed to saturate the external environment with the critical substances and so permit internal accumulation will depend on how fast the substances can be produced. Obviously, if each cell produces them at a constant rate, two cells will produce twice as much per unit time as will one and therefore do the job in half the time, i.e., many cells inoculated into a given volume of fresh medium can begin growing very quickly, whereas a few cells in the same medium would take a much longer time or might never get started at all.

Cooperative interactions also occur between embryonic cells. For example, if we cut out a large piece of dorsal ectoderm from a chick or mouse embryo and cultivate it in a dish with appropriate nutrients, the tissue will yield nerve cells just as it would if left in the embryo. If, however, a single large piece is cut up into many small pieces and each is cultivated separately, no nerve cells appear. The mere act of cutting does not affect the result, because if the small pieces are cultivated together in a compact mass, they produce nerve cells as efficiently as one large piece does. Thus, many cells can do what few cannot, in this case become transformed into specialized nerve cells. We have already examined other developments of this kind in nonembryonic material. Thus, large pieces of stems of *Acetabularia* or of coelenterates regenerate head parts more rapidly and completely than do small pieces.

INDUCTIVE INTERACTIONS

The Embryonic Organizer

The most complex inductive mechanisms are found in vertebrate embryos; one example is the *embryonic organizer* demonstrated by Dr. H. Spemann, one of the founders of modern embryology. Spemann was interested in the problem of whether fragments of an embryo could contain or produce all the cell types necessary for the construction of a complete, normal adult (see Chapter 6). He cut salamander embryos in half at various stages of development and found that, before gastrulation, both halves yielded normal adults but that after gastrulation both developed aberrantly. To fix the point at which the capacity for normal development was lost, Spemann cut embryos in half at various times during gastrulation and, to his surprise, one of the halves invariably gave rise to a complete, normal embryo, while the other yielded a degenerate, amorphous cell mass. Upon closer examination, he found that the half yielding a normal product was always the one that contained the dorsal lip of the blastopore.* It appeared from these results that: (1) cells from the dorsal lip have the power to organize or initiate the construction of the embryo, and (2) no other cells can do this—if the dorsal lip is absent, therefore, embryonic organization does not occur.

To confirm that dorsal-lip cells, called *prospective chorda-mesoderm,* were the inducers of the embryonic organization, Spemann cut out pieces of this tissue and implanted them in the ventral sides of other gastrulas (in contrast to the position that chorda-mesoderm normally occupies, i.e., under the dorsal ectoderm). Two results were observed:

1. At the site of implantation, a small but perfect embryo developed as a sort of Siamese twin of the host embryo. Brain, spinal cord, and associated organs were present.

2. The implanted chorda-mesoderm went ahead and developed precisely as it would have had it been in its normal position in the embryo; that is, it constructed a notochord and somites. In contrast, any other part of the gastrula, when implanted in this manner, did not develop as it would have if it had not been moved, but instead developed in accordance with its new locale.

The second result showed that indeed there was something special about dorsal-lip tissue. The first result revealed that dorsal-lip cells could induce overlying ectoderm to form brain, nerve cord, and associated parts. When that part of the dorsal-lip tissue that normally underlies the brain was implanted, it induced brain development very well and tail development very poorly, and when posterior chorda-mesoderm was implanted, it induced tail very well and brain very poorly. Thus the chorda-mesoderm is a specific inducer.

The main question, of course, is, what compound or compounds does the chorda-mesoderm supply to the overlying ectoderm to produce the

* You will recall from Chapter 6 that the blastopore is the crescent-shaped hole through which the cells invaginate from the surface to the interior of the embryo. Cells at the upper, or dorsal, lip of the blastopore move inside and take up residence directly under that part of the ectoderm that will later give rise to the central nervous system. They become the central part of the mesoderm and give rise to notochord and somites.

organization of the ectoderm tissue? Unfortunately, any of a wide variety of substances from many sources has been found to do this, so wide in fact that the induction appears to have very little specificity. It is almost as if the ectoderm at this stage of development is a gun primed to shoot in a fixed direction and needing only a touch on the trigger to set it off. This "sensitivity" raises two other very interesting questions.

1. Although it is true that the embryologist can make ectoderm organize itself by treating it with a wide variety of agents, in the actual embryo only dorsal-lip cells can do this. What, then, passes between the chorda-mesoderm and the overlying ectoderm? To answer this question, one might label the constituents of dorsal-lip cells with radioactive carbon or sulfur or phosphorus and thus determine what materials pass from the "hot" mesodermal cells to the "cold" ectodermal cells.

2. If it is true that the embryologist can cause ectoderm to organize itself by applying many agents, why in an actual embryo does only one part of the ectoderm normally become organized into brain and spinal cord? Why aren't secondary embryos caused to pop out all over the place, having been induced by any of the multitude of materials that normally leak out of cells? Here we return to the problem of the *morphogenetic field* discussed in Chapter 5.

Secondary Inducers in Embryos

As we just described, dorsal-lip tissue induces overlying ectoderm to transform into brain and nerve cord, while it itself forms notochord and somites. From this point on, many contiguous tissues provide one another with inductive signals that trigger the formation of additional organs. In general, the proof that such inductions operate has fallen into two categories: Investigators have shown (a) that if tissue A is removed or physically separated from tissue B, tissue B will not construct a specific organ as it usually does; and (b) that if tissue A is moved to a neighboring spot occupied by cells closely allied to B, the organ in question will form at the new site occupied by tissue A and not at the old.

Figure 7-1 is a schematic and partial summary of the manifold inductive relationships uncovered in this manner. In some cases, these inductions have, by and large, proved to be much more specific than that supplied by the embryonic organizer. However, little of the rigorous biochemistry needed to shed light on them has been performed so far.

Cell Interactions During Limb Development

In a three-day-old chick embryo, the limb bud is a simple outpocketing of ectoderm filled with a mesodermal core. At this time the two tissue components may be separated cleanly. If they are put back together again and grafted on to the flank of a host embryo, a normal limb develops complete with articulating digits, etc. It is also possible, however, to graft these components separately or in combination with various nonlimb tissues. The results of such experiments are summarized below:

1. If cultivated separately, neither limb-bud ectoderm nor limb-bud mesoderm yields a limb

2. Limb-bud ectoderm plus nonlimb-bud mesoderm = no limb development
   Nonlimb ectoderm plus limb-bud mesoderm = no limb development

3. Wing-bud ectoderm plus leg-bud mesoderm = a leg
   Leg-bud ectoderm plus wing-bud mesoderm = a wing

4. Normal limb-bud ectoderm plus limb-bud mesoderm from a mutant chick (which develops extra digits on its limbs = a mutant limb
   Mutant limb-bud ectoderm plus normal limb-bud mesoderm = a normal limb

Fig. 7-1. Inductive relationships between different parts of the developing embryo. (After Holtfreter.) Arrows point from the inducing tissues to the induced organ that ultimately appears. Bear in mind that this array of inductions is far from complete.

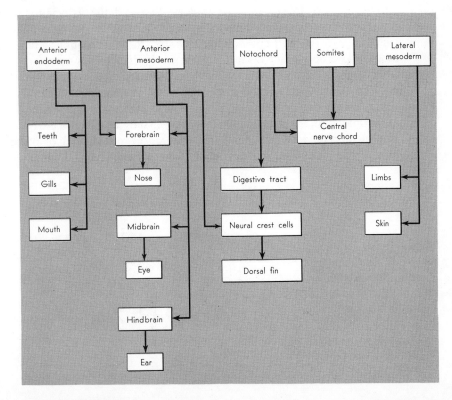

These results indicate that both the ectodermal and mesodermal components are required for limb development but the kind of limb produced depends on the genetic constitution of the mesoderm (whether mutant or normal) as well as the area of the embryo from which the mesoderm was taken (whether wing-bud or leg-bud). The development of the limb therefore results from specific interactions between these two tissues.

SYNERGISTIC INDUCTIONS

Synergistic inductions are those in which two different tissues mutually interact so that each causes the other to develop in a way that it would not alone. For example, the developing kidney contains many small S-shaped *secretory tubules* connected to a fan-like network of branched *collecting tubes* that serve to transport material collected by the secretory tubules into the ureter to be voided as urine. Figure 7-2 is a schematic diagram of kidney-tubule development. The tubes and tubules originate from two different rudimentary tissues, starting at about the eleventh day of embryonic life; these are the *nephrogenic cord,* a loose collection of mesodermal cells, and the *ureteric bud,* a compact tubular tissue also derived from mesoderm. The development of the secretory tubules from the former and the collecting tubes from the latter has been found to depend on the intimate association of both. Removal of either from the embryo stops the development of the other.

It is possible to separate the ureteric bud and the associated nephrogenic cord from a mouse embryo and cultivate the tissues on a blood clot overlain with a nutrient solution. Under these conditions, tubes and tubules develop as they do in the embryo. If the two tissues are separated from each other and cultivated, tubes and tubules never develop. Many unsuccessful attempts have been made to extract material from either tissue, that, when added to a culture of the other, would make it develop in normal fashion. If, however, the two tissues are separated by a very thin membrane with tiny holes, the synergistic induction does occur. Although the membrane is thick enough to prevent the two kinds of cells

Fig. 7-2. Formation of kidney tubules. (After Arey.) See text for descriptive details.

Collecting tube

from touching, blobs of cytoplasm could conceivably pass between the two. When opposed across thicker membranes, synergistic development does not occur.

This type of induction is a common phenomenon in developmental systems. It requires the reacting tissues to remain in intimate association for long periods of time. Many chemical explanations can be imagined to account for induction by direct contact but, as in much of what we have already described, the necessary biochemical analyses are only now beginning to be made.

INHIBITORY INTERACTIONS

As we stressed in Chapter 5, all morphogenetic fields involve inhibition —i.e., cells in one part of the field develop in a certain manner and simultaneously inhibit the surrounding cells from doing so. This is the case in hydranth development in coelenterates, bud development in plants, the construction of the head, heart, limbs, and eyes in vertebrate embryos, etc. As we mentioned in Chapter 5, inhibition can conceivably exist at two levels:

1. Where competition for a common store of materials in the environment enables only the cells that receive the greatest supply to develop.
2. Where the production of material by one cell inhibits another.

KNOWN MECHANISMS OF CELL INTERACTION

Space limits us to only a few examples of known mechanisms by which one cell can influence the growth and development of another. We have drawn these from experiments with microorganisms which, being simpler to manipulate and easier to grow under defined conditions, permit of more rigorous analyses at present than more complex organisms do. Unfortunately, these experiments involve only single-celled organisms and thus their interactions can serve merely as models for similar interactions among the cells of higher plants and animals.

Selective Inhibition During Bacterial Growth

The bacterium *Brucella abortus* causes aborting fever in cattle and Brucellosis in man. When *B. abortus* is taken from the blood of a diseased animal and grown on an agar medium, it forms a colony with a very even outline and mucoid texture, because each cell in the colony is surrounded by a polysaccharide capsule. This type of colony is called "smooth," and the constituent cells are called S-cells. During the growth of S-cells, rare mutations occur that prevent the mutant and its offspring from synthesizing a capsule. The mutants are called R-cells, and since the colonies derived from them possess an uneven outline and wrinkled appearance, they are called "rough."

If we inoculate a flask of nutrient broth with S-cells, we find that by the time growth has ceased, the population is no longer composed only of S-cells but now has a great majority of R-cells. Figure 7-3 summarizes the results. The total population grows normally until the fourth day of incubation, then it dips quickly, begins to grow again, and finally reaches

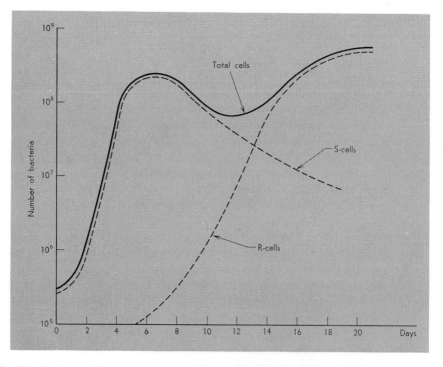

Fig. 7-3. Selective inhibition as evidenced during the growth of Brucella abortus **cells.**

a stationary state. Until the fourth day, the population is made up almost completely of S-type cells. After 4 days, these decline rapidly. R-cells make their appearance coincidentally with the decline of S-cells, increase rapidly, and by 20 days make up over 90 per cent of the population.

As the bacteria grow, intracellular substances leak into the broth; one of these substances is the amino acid alanine ($CH_3 \cdot CH \cdot NH_2 \cdot COOH$). The appearance of alanine coincides with the decline of the S-cells. The

S-cells are very sensitive to alanine and die in its presence, whereas R-cells are resistant to it and can grow normally. Thus, by the fourth day, the S-cells have produced enough alanine to be poisoned by it. In the meantime, a few R-cells have arisen by mutation. Since the S-cells cannot grow, the R-cells do and eventually dominate the population. The proportion of R- and S-cells is controlled at any time by the levels of alanine.

The interaction between the two cell types, therefore, is not simply the result of an exchange of materials between the two. The S-cells, by acting upon themselves (i.e., committing suicide), permit the R-cells to do something they ordinarily could not have done, namely grow. (Had the S-cells not died out, there would have been no opportunity for the R-cells to grow.)

Transformation of Cell Types in *Diplococcus Pneumoniae*

The bacterium *D. pneumoniae* gives rise to mutant types that are different in many ways from the parental stock. For example, we can isolate mutants that are resistant to penicillin or streptomycin (when the parent type is sensitive to these antibiotics), mutants that can degrade sugars that the parent type is incapable of degrading, and mutants that require various compounds for growth that the parent type can make for itself.

Highly purified deoxyribose nucleic acid (DNA) has been prepared from penicillin-resistant mutant cells. When the sensitive parental type is exposed to this DNA, a large proportion of the cells are transformed into the penicillin-resistant type, and what's more, they pass on this new capacity to their offspring. The DNA can only cause the exposed cells to acquire capacities that are possessed by the cells from which the DNA was obtained (i.e., DNA from penicillin-sensitive bacteria never transforms the exposed cells to penicillin-resistant varieties). In essence, then, it is possible to extract genetic information from one cell and introduce it into another. The macromolecule bearing this information can be incorporated into the genetic apparatus of the treated cell, and thus the information is passed on to the progeny.

Synergistic Growth by Biochemically Deficient Mutants

We deal here indirectly with some of the most important genetic experiments of our time, those conducted upon the bread mold *Neurospora crassa*. They are so important because, among other things, they provided convincing proof that genes act by controlling the synthesis of specific enzymes.

Neurospora crassa can be grown on a relatively simple medium containing glucose as a source of carbon and energy, ammonium chloride as a source of nitrogen, a few mineral salts, and two vitamins. In these experiments, mutants were isolated, that, unlike the parental type, had to be supplied with various compounds in order to grow because they could not synthesize the compounds; some examples are histidineless mutants (which cannot synthesize histidine and will not grow unless supplied with it) and thiamineless, riboflavinless, and tryptophaneless mutants, and many others. These are called *biochemically deficient mutants.*

In all cases, the mutant lacks a single enzyme necessary for the synthesis of a particular cell constituent. Amino acids, vitamins, etc., are generally synthesized in stepwise fashion from a pool of common, simple substances in a manner shown symbolically below:

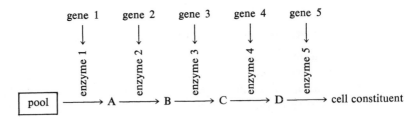

The absence of enzyme 2 would eliminate the reaction A ⟶ B and thus prevent the production of intermediates B, C, D, and the final product. If gene 2 in the nucleus mutated to a nonfunctional form (i.e., one unable to direct the synthesis of enzyme 2), the mutant cell would be unable to synthesize the final product and would grow only when it was supplied in the culture medium. Two predictions can be made for such mutants. These predictions, which turn out to be true, are:

1. That the mutant lacking enzyme 2 could still grow if supplied with the final product, or with intermediates B, C, or D, since the cell can convert these into the final product.

2. That intermediate A would accumulate in the mutant cell, since the reaction A ⟶ B is blocked. Because these intermediates are generally of low molecular weight and are readily diffusible, they not only accumulate inside the mutant cell but usually seep out of the cell into the surrounding medium.

Synergistic growth of deficient mutants occurs because of this osmotic property. As an example, we shall consider biochemically deficient mutants of the bacterium *Escherichia coli,* which are all arginineless (unable to synthesize the essential amino acid arginine). Arginine is normally synthesized via the following pathway:

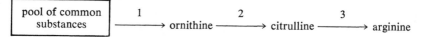

Three kinds of mutants have been isolated. It was found that:

Mutant 1 could grow if supplied with ornithine, citrulline, or arginine (i.e., the enzyme that catalyzes reaction 1 is missing).

Mutant 2 could grow if supplied with citrulline or arginine, but *not* if supplied with ornithine; however, ornithine accumulated in the cells and seeped out into the medium (i.e., the enzyme-catalyzing reaction 2 was missing).

Mutant 3 could grow only if supplied with arginine, *not* with ornithine or citrulline; however, citrulline accumulated in the cells and seeped out into the medium (i.e., the enzyme-catalyzing reaction 3 was missing).

If, as shown in Fig. 7-4, the three mutant types are streaked on agar containing a tiny amount of arginine, synergistic growth occurs. Mutant 3 grows very sparingly until the arginine in the medium is used up, and then it stops. It continues, however, to generate energy by oxidation and to carry out a wide variety of biochemical reactions, including the synthesis of citrulline, which accumulates and seeps out into the medium. Mutant 2, growing nearby, can convert the citrulline to arginine. Since mutant 3 makes a large quantity of citrulline, mutant 2 can grow very well. If the mutant 2 cells do not lie next to mutant 3, they grow very sparingly, but

Fig. 7-4. Synergistic growth by three mutant types of E. coli. **Shading indicates growth; no shading, no growth.**

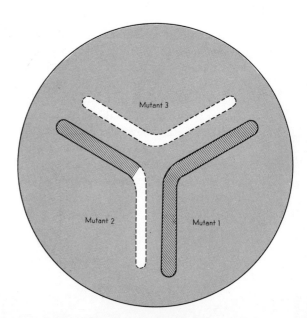

they still can metabolize and accumulate ornithine. Since mutant 1 can convert both citrulline or ornithine to the needed final product, it grows very well if it is streaked next to either mutant 2 or mutant 3. In multicellular organisms, the various tissues may well influence the growth of neighboring cells in just this manner. There are numerous examples in embryonic development of the effect of one organ or tissue upon the growth of another.

CONCLUSION

Every cell in nature interacts with other cells. Sister microbial cells compete for food and space, and sometimes exert direct inhibitory effects on one another in order to survive the competition. They can also assist one another by exchange of metabolites. Genetic information can be transferred from one to another and produce new capacities in the recipients. In multicellular forms, where the constituent cells are packed together in a compact mass, opportunities for cell interaction are numerous and, since developmental activities must be timed perfectly, are even more necessary than in single-celled organisms. The kinds of interaction can be classed as follows:

1. Population-density effects—where many cells of the same kind cooperate to do something that few together could not do.
2. Inductive interactions.
3. Synergistic inductions.
4. Inhibitory interactions.

The vehicles of interaction seem to fall into these categories:

1. Interactions promoted by diffusible agents among cells separated from one another. Such agents can be carried by simple diffusion or transported through the circulatory system.
2. Direct-contact interactions. Such systems probably require intimate contact because the material transferred is very unstable and will not survive transport over great distances or because large amounts of cytoplasm are exchanged and several substances must travel as a unit.
3. Contact interactions without exchange of material. The surface of one cell may react with that of another to create drastic surface alterations, which are then reflected by secondary changes in the metabolism of the cell.

Cellular
Differentiation:
Descriptions

CHAPTER EIGHT

Chapters 8 and 9 focus upon the phenomenon of cellular differentiation, dealing first with several different pathways of differentiation as they occur in vertebrate and invertebrate embryos and second with our current understanding of the mechanisms involved.

DEVELOPMENT OF THE BRISTLE ORGAN IN THE FRUIT FLY

Professor Curt Stern, one of the fathers of modern genetics, in his article * entitled "Two or Three Bristles," has a superb discussion of cellular differentiation that is designed to be read by scientists who are not biologists; it can easily be understood and will be greatly appreciated by serious beginning students of biology.

To illustrate the problems inherent in cellular differentiation, Dr. Stern describes the formation of bristles on the abdomen of the fruit fly:

* Published in *American Scientist,* April 1, 1954.

In some regions there arise short or long outgrowths—the bristles—strong and wide at the base and gently tapering to a fine point. Narrow grooves, as in fluted columns with a slightly baroque twist, extend along their lengths. A short stalk fits each bristle into a round socket within the body armor so that the bristle can be moved within this articulation. . . . The bristles are tiny sense organs, perhaps sensitive to the fluctuations of air pressure when the fly is in flight.

Dr. Stern goes on to describe the cellular structure of the bristle organ. It consists of three cells: the bristle cell itself, which secretes the tapered outgrowth; the socket cell that secretes a socket-like ring of hard chitin into which the base of the bristle fits; and, below these two, a sensory nerve cell that is linked to the bristle by a short nerve fiber and whose other long nerve fiber connects up with the central nervous system, thereby communicating stimuli from the bristle.

The three bristle organ cells come from a single ancestor. At first, the thoracic epidermis is simply a continuous sheet of many identical cells. Then at a fixed stage in the development of the young adult from the immature larva, single cells within the sheet grow to giant size. Division occurs and one daughter cell is changed into a sensory nerve cell. The other daughter divides again, one half becoming the bristle-forming cell, the other the socket-forming cell. See Fig. 8-1 for the lineage.

It should be noted that a fixed number of giant cells appear in the thoracic epidermis and always at specific points, thus yielding a precise pattern. There are mutant fruit flies, however, that display different numbers and patterns of bristles, and as one would expect in these organisms, the number and positions of the giant cells differ from the norm. In addition, some mutants produce bristles of different shape and size or produce none at all. These abnormalities, too, can be traced back to specific events in the early development of the fly. For example, in one of the types that produce no bristles, the giant cells arise at the right time and place and each divides into two. One of the daughters as usual becomes a nerve cell and the other divides as it should. But instead of yielding a bristle and a socket cell, two socket cells appear!

This research raises many questions. What genetic and biochemical processes cause one cell among many suddenly to become a giant? Why does it appear here and not there? Why, having produced three daughter cells, does cell division stop? What causes three cells with the same parentage to be transformed into totally different individuals?

THE DEVELOPMENT OF NEURAL TISSUE

Cellular differentiation, as we see it in bristle formation, occurs in every developmental system, whether it be slime mold, coelenterate, or human

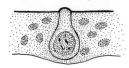

1. Giant cell appears

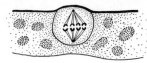

2. Giant cell divides

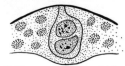

3. Divisions are complete, yielding prenerve cell below and parent of socket and bristle cells above

4. Upper cell proceeds through mitosis

5. Division of upper cell yields the bristle and socket cells

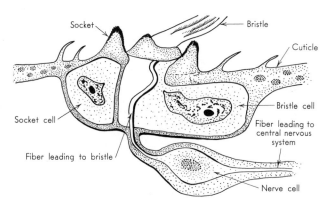

6. A semidiagrammatic drawing of the functional bristle apparatus

Fig. 8-1. Development of the bristle organ. (Adapted from C. Stern.)

being. Each stage of development is accompanied by the appearance of new cell types that play a direct role in the formation of the adult structure. Some of these cells, like the giant bristle cell in the fruit fly, perform a specific act and then do one of three things: die, divide, or simply become unimportant for further development. Others, like the nerve cell in the bristle organ, persist and play a role in the subsequent functioning of the adult. Figure 8-2 summarizes a more complicated series of cellular differentiations in the vertebrate embryo. All the cell types shown arise in the neural tube in the region of the brain. They are descended from ectodermal cells that inhabited the dorsal area of the embryo after gastrulation. Only those cells that remain in the inner core of the neural tube continue to reproduce actively and to resemble their parents. Those cells that are pushed toward the periphery cease dividing and are transformed into the types illustrated in Fig. 8-2. It should be realized that the drastic morpho-

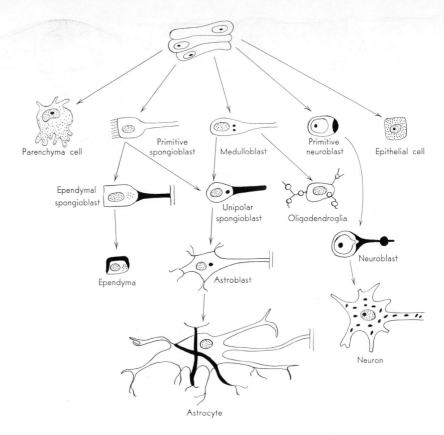

Fig. 8-2. The main cell types that arise from neural epithelial tissue. (After P. A. Weiss.)

logical changes shown are reflections of equally drastic changes in the metabolic capabilities of these cells.

THE DEVELOPMENT OF MAMMALIAN RED BLOOD CELLS

The normal human red blood cell (*erythrocyte*) is a biconcave disc, 8 μ in diameter and 2 μ thick at the edge. It is little more than a bag of hemoglobin (the body's oxygen carrier), a protein that occurs in the mature erythrocyte at a concentration equivalent to a 30 per cent solution. The erythrocyte is bounded by a lipoprotein membrane and contains a reticulated fibrous network plus a trace of proteins other than hemoglobin.

Figure 8-3 shows the development of the erythrocyte from an ameba-like parental cell, the *hemocytoblast*. It is interesting that 3 kinds of *leukocytes* (white blood cells) are also derived from this cell group; therefore, development into a red blood cell must first involve some kind of choice, which is probably dictated by environmental conditions. As shown in Fig. 8-3, the hemocytoblast gives rise via mitosis to morphologically altered cells called *erythroblasts*. These cells, which begin to synthesize hemoglobin at a low rate, in turn undergo further changes to become *normoblasts*. Normal mitotic cell divisions have continued up to this point, but now the nucleus degenerates and either disappears or is extruded. Thus, the final form of the mature erythrocyte is attained. It should be emphasized that the bulk of hemoglobin synthesis takes place *after* the degeneration and disappearance of the nucleus. In fact, virtually 100 per cent of the synthetic machinery of the cell is devoted to hemoglobin synthesis at this time. Thus, the instructions for hemoglobin manufacture must be sent out into the erythrocyte cytoplasm by the genes responsible *before* the nucleus disappears and those instructions must be conserved long afterwards. The erythrocyte is actually a transitory cell; it has an

Fig. 8-3. Erythrocyte development. Shadings of gray indicate change from pale to deep red. (After Maximow and Bloom.)

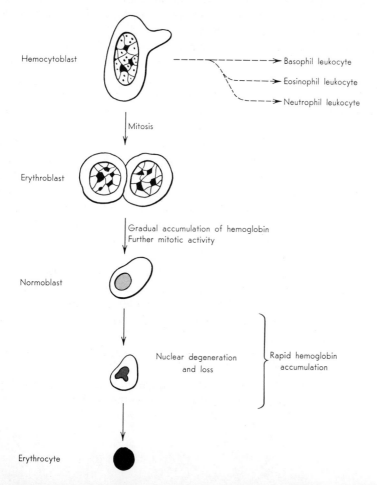

average lifespan of 120 days in human beings, after which it travels to the spleen and is destroyed.

The hemocytoblasts arise from a common source in mammalian embryos, i.e., from loose wandering ameboid cells that originally split off from the mesoderm. Some of these wanderers are part of the extra embryonic tissues (like yolk sac) that serve the developing embryo and are discarded shortly before or at birth. The extra embryonic wandering cells give rise to primitive blood cells that serve to carry oxygen to the young embryo but later disappear. Other hemocytoblasts take up residence and grow in the developing spleen, liver, and bone marrow. The first two organs supply large numbers of erythrocytes during embryogenesis, but ultimately, in the young animal and adult, the primary source is the bone marrow.

As mentioned, the primary if not sole biochemical end product of this pathway of differentiation is hemoglobin itself. It is a globular protein with a molecular weight of about 68,000 (in human beings) and contains about 600 amino acids. The hemoglobin macromolecule is fabricated from 4 separate polypeptide chains interwoven to yield a roughly spherical mass plus 4 molecules of an iron-porphyrin compound called *heme;* the latter are attached to the chains and serve as binding sites for oxygen.

Of the 4 polypeptide chains, 2 are identical molecules, i.e., identical in composition and position of amino acids. They are called α-polypeptides. The other two chains are also identical with each other and are called β-polypeptides. Thus, the protein portion of hemoglobin can be written as: $\alpha_2\beta_2$.

Actually there are two varieties of hemoglobin in normal human beings, *fetal* and *adult*. The first is made during embryonic development and in young infants. The second begins to accumulate in the latter stages of embryogenesis and gradually assumes the dominant role. Fetal hemoglobin disappears usually in the first year or two. Its molecular composition is like that of the adult variety except that a different polypeptide chain called γ is in the place of the β-polypeptide. Thus, its protein composition can be written as: $\alpha_2\gamma_2$.

Genetic studies have shown that at least three genes control the protein portion of hemoglobin synthesis, each one providing the instructions for the synthesis of a single variety of polypeptide. Thus the "α" and "γ" genes function to produce fetal hemoglobin, the "α" and "β" genes to produce adult hemoglobin.

To summarize, the steps involved in erythrocyte development are as follows:

1. The parental cells grow and divide, undergo a series of morphological (and biochemical) alterations, and begin to synthesize hemoglobin. In the

fetus, the α and γ genes become active at this stage of blood cell development. Presumably in the adult the α and β genes begin to function at this time, supplying the instructions necessary for the fabrication of the corresponding polypeptides.

2. The developing erythrocyte now loses its nucleus and attains its final form. It has become a factory whose sole product is hemoglobin, it having dispensed with all extraneous cellular activities.

3. After a transitory existence, the erythrocyte is destroyed.

THE DIFFERENTIATION OF PANCREATIC CELLS IN THE MOUSE

The pancreas first emerges during embryogenesis as a rudimentary process budded off from the duodenal portion of the intestine. At 11 days it consists of a bulb-shaped layer of closely attached cells (the epithelial component) plus an associated mass of loosely attached cells (the mesenchymal component). Starting at the eleventh day, the latter provides a specific chemical stimulus that induces the former to increase in size, become lobed, and give rise to *Acinar cells*. These cells, later on have the special job of excreting into the intestines digestive enzymes such as amylase (which is responsible for converting starch to maltose).

Figure 8-4 shows the temporal course of events leading to the appearance of Acinar cells. These are summarized below:

1. *Induction.* In the absence of the mesenchyme, the epithelium fails to grow, lobulate, or produce Acinar cells. But, starting at 11 days, if the two tissues remain in contact for at least 40 hours, normal development will occur despite subsequent removal of the mesenchyme. Thus, during contact the reacting tissue has become committed.

2. *Growth.* Cells at the surface of the rudiment grow and divide. (Those daughter cells that slip below the surface cease division while those that remain there continue to do so.)

3. *Appearance of ribosomes and endoplasmic reticulum.* * Ribosomes accumulate suddenly and in great numbers. This event generally indicates a period of rapid and extensive protein synthesis in a cell. Then the ribosomes become integrated into the endoplasmic reticulum. This structure is characteristic of cells that make large amounts of specialized materials for export (like extracellular enzymes and hormones).

4. *Appearance of amylase.* This enzyme appears suddenly and increases enormously in concentration over a period of 3–4 days.

5. *Appearance of zymogen granules.* These appear shortly after the ac-

---

* See C. P. Swanson, *The Cell,* 2nd ed. (Englewood Cliffs, N. J.: Prentice-Hall, 1964), for detailed description of these structures.

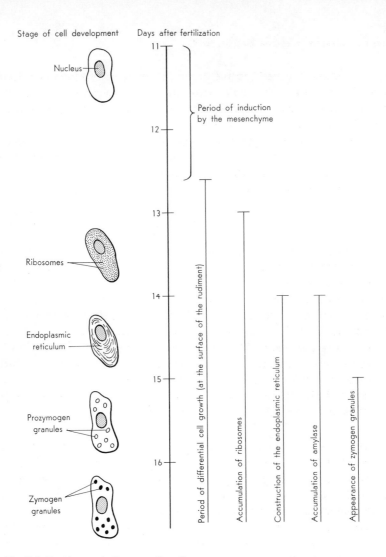

Fig. 8-4. Development of pancreatic cells.

cumulation of amylase. They are organized packages of enzymes including amylase that will be exported into the intestine to be used for food digestion.

CONCLUSION

In a developing multicellular assembly, whether it be slime mold, coelenterate, or man, the cells acquire new biochemical and morphological properties and lose old ones. In the words of the geneticist, the developing cells undergo changes in phenotype (i.e., observable morphological and biochemical properties). These phenotypic changes are marked by the following characteristics.

1. In general, phenotypic changes in differentiating cells are not the result of random, internal, physiological variations. They are *directed changes specifically induced by environmental stimuli.*

2. In general, the environmental stimulus must be applied at a *particular time in the developmental history of the cell and need then be applied for only a limited time, after which the differentiating cells become committed and hence independent of the presence of the external stimulus.*

3. Phenotypic changes, characteristic of cellular differentiation, are not simple, unique events leading, for example, to the presence or absence of a single enzyme. *A differentiating cell undergoes a complex sequence of biochemical and morphological changes, the sum of which leaves it drastically altered in form and function.*

4. These events are under strict control with respect to *time, place,* and *quantity:*

Time: They occur in a definite, invariant temporal order.

Place: The direction in which a given cell will differentiate is determined by its position in the multicellular assembly.

Quantity: The numbers of cells entering into the various pathways of differentiation bear fixed relations to one another.

Cellular Differentiation: Mechanisms

CHAPTER NINE

THE GENETIC BASIS OF CELLULAR DIFFERENTIATION

When we say that cells undergo alterations in structural and metabolic capabilities and/or give rise to altered progeny, it is the ears of the geneticist that perk up most sharply. For the possibility arises that the genetic endowment of that cell or of its progeny has been altered. To understand this statement, we must review briefly the modern concept of heredity.*

The genetic endowment of a cell is a collection of macromolecules containing sets of instructions for fabricating the remainder of the cell constituents. The ultimate source of these instructions—hence, the hereditary material—is DNA, whose structure is illustrated schematically in Fig. 9-1. Its backbone consists of two chains, wound in spirals. Each chain is composed of alternating molecules of a sugar

---

* For a detailed discussion of these matters, see D. M. Bonner and S. Mills, *Heredity,* 2nd ed. (Englewood Cliffs, N. J.: Prentice-Hall, 1964).

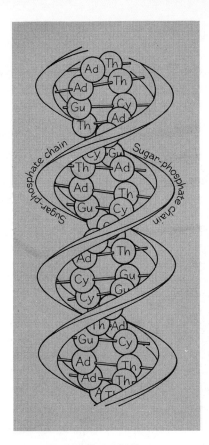

Fig. 9-1. The structure of DNA.

(deoxyribose) and phosphate. Attached to each sugar is one of four molecules: the purine bases adenine (A) and guanine (G) and the pyrimidine bases thymine (T) and cytosine (C). The chains are held together in the helix by low energy forces exerted between the paired bases. DNA must perform two tasks:

1. *It must guide the synthesis of an exact copy prior to cell division so that the daughter cells will inherit identical sets of instructions.* This is assured by the fact that, within the helical arrangement of the two strands, adenine is always found opposite thymine and guanine always opposite cytosine. Thus, reading from the top of Fig. 9-1, the sequence AAGT in one strand must pair with TTCA in the other. The strands are therefore said to be complementary. During the duplication of DNA, each separate strand serves as a model for the construction of its complement by the enzyme DNA polymerase, as shown below. In this manner a single set of instructions can give rise to two identical sets.

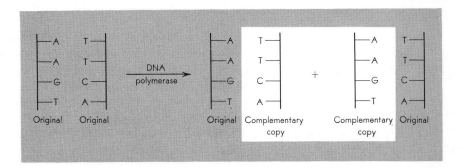

2. It must serve as a blueprint, providing instructions for the fabrication of protein molecules within a cell. The four bases A, G, T, and C are the letters of the genetic dictionary. They are put together into words and the words into sentences. Each gene is one sentence that provides the information for the fabrication of a particular protein by dictating the number of amino acids, the different kinds, and the order in which they are strung together. The biological activity of the protein is in turn dictated by its amino acid composition. Thus, for example, the gene controlling the ability of a microorganism to hydrolyze lactose does so by determining the order of the amino acids in a particular protein. This order uniquely qualifies the protein to act as the enzyme for binding with lactose and splitting it into the constituent sugars. Other genes guide the synthesis of other proteins. Ultimately the complete range of structural and biochemical capabilities of the cell is governed by the kinds of proteins it contains (that is to say, its enzymatic capacities).

Genetic information provides the cell with the potential for making a variety of cell constituents and for performing many functions. However, that a cell is genetically equipped to carry out a particular activity does not guarantee that it will do so, for the environment in which it lives also tells the cell what it can and cannot do. Two examples are provided to show what this statement means:

1. *Euglena* is a protozoan-like organism that is capable of photosynthesis, containing about 10 chloroplasts per cell. When grown in the dark, where it generates energy not by photosynthesis but by oxidation of organic nutrients, the chloroplasts disappear. The instructions for making chloroplasts are still intact, but whether the cell does make them is decided by the light; when *Euglena* is once again exposed to light, chloroplasts are again formed.

2. The lymphoid tissue of an animal exposed to diphtheria toxin will form antibodies (proteins that specifically neutralize the toxin). Although the genetic potential for making antibodies is ever present, only exposure to the foreign toxin can trigger antibody synthesis.

In brief, then, what a cell can do is determined by its genetic endowment, i.e., the instructions provided by its genetic material. The geneticist terms this endowment the *genotype*. The cell's actual activity is the result of the interaction between the genetic potential of the cell and the environment in which the cell finds itself. What the cell does (i.e., its structure and metabolic capacities) is termed the *phenotype*.

Faced with the fact that during the development of a multicellular organism, daughter cells can gain new capacities or lose old ones and so become different both from their parents and from their sisters, we must ascribe the change to one or both of two processes:

1. The daughter cell receives from the parent its genetic endowment intact and unchanged. The environment in which it must live, however, is different from that which the parent cell faced. Consequently, it synthesizes cell constituents that its parent did not and vice versa. The altered metabolism leads to morphological differences as well.

2. The genetic endowment of the daughter cell is different from that of the parent. Thus, the act of cellular differentiation would involve a change in the primary genetic material and the alteration would be inherited by the progeny, if any, of the differentiated cell. The genetic macromolecules being altered, the enzymes constructed under their direction would be altered in quantity or kind. In this manner, the altered genotype becomes amplified into an altered phenotype.

This second process, though not given in chemical terms, was implicitly contained in an early theory offered by A. Weismann in 1900. Weismann proposed that, when a fertilized egg cleaved, daughter cells did not receive identical sets of genetic determinants. Instead, these were parceled out in a regular fashion depending on the location of the cell in the embryo, so that different cells received different genetic endowments. The difference in genetic content would account for cellular differentiation. The parceling out according to location would insure normality of form. Figure 9-2 is a summary of this scheme in which the original egg cell contains all the genetic elements necessary to make a complete embryo. After cleavage, its descendants not only contain different sets of genetic elements, but the necessary cell types end up in the right places in the embryo. Weismann realized that the embryo would ultimately become an adult animal, that it would produce eggs or sperm, and that these would necessarily have to contain all the genetic elements to make the next generation of embryos. He made provision for this by adding the qualification that during cleavage a few cells would inherit a complete set of genetic elements (see Fig. 9-2) and that these would become the gametes of the future adult.

In order to test this hypothesis, biologists permitted fertilized eggs to cleave into 2, 4, 8, 16, or more cells and then removed some of them. If all the cells had inherited a complete set of instructions for making an embryo, the loss of a few cells would not be expected to matter. In contrast, if most of the cells received an incomplete set of instructions, the removal of some cells would remove certain instructions that the other cells lacked and an incomplete embryo would result. Experiments of this kind have tended to group embryos into two categories. If we permit a

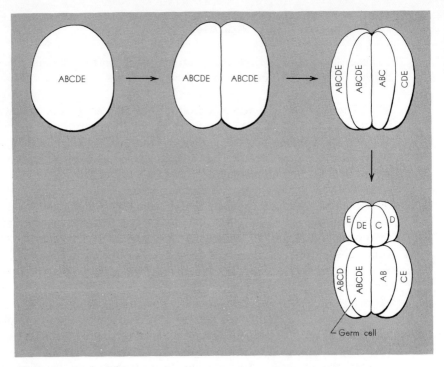

Fig. 9-2. A schematic illustration of Weismann's hypothesis (the segregation of genetic elements).

fertilized egg to cleave into two blastomeres and then separate them, each will, it is true, produce a complete embryo. But, if the egg happens to be from a clam, starfish, sea urchin, or comb jelly, this capacity disappears rapidly. That is, once the egg has cleaved into 8 or 16 or 32 cells and some of these are removed, the remaining cells form an incomplete embryo, with specific parts missing according to which of the cells were removed. (This is called *mosaic* development.) In contrast, the embryos of frogs, salamanders, and chicks are more malleable. Portions of the early frog embryo can be removed without reducing its capacity to turn out a normal product. The remaining cells simply take over the functions of the missing ones. (This is called *regulative* development.) But even here, if we wait long enough and permit the embryo to develop far enough, removal will result in incomplete development. We might conclude from the above that, during development, the cells remaining after excision had lost the potential capacity to replace the missing contingent. But we can equally well imagine that by the time the excision is made, the environmental conditions no longer permit the change of a cell from one type to another.

In recent years an elegant set of experiments have shown that cell nuclei taken from late embryonic stages are no longer equivalent to the

102

nucleus of the egg cell from which they were derived. A frog egg was enucleated; that is, the nucleus was removed with a microtool. It was replaced with a nucleus taken from a cell at the blastula or gastrula or neurula stage of frog embryogenesis. In other words, the egg cytoplasm was combined with a nucleus representative of cells that had already become differentiated. This synthetic egg was then allowed to develop in order to determine the degree of normality and completeness achieved (see Fig. 9-3).

When a blastula nucleus was added to the enucleated egg, a normal embryo resulted. When nuclei from later stages were employed, nearly all the resulting embryos were grossly abnormal. Most important, the kind of abnormality observed depended on the part of the embryo from which the nucleus had been taken. Thus, an endoderm nucleus added to the enucleated egg gave rise to an embryo whose structures derived from endoderm were normal, but whose other structures were abnormal. A mesoderm nucleus yielded an embryo whose mesodermal development was normal, but whose other parts were abnormal. Yet a small proportion of the eggs bearing nuclei from later embryonic stages did in fact develop into normal embryos. Furthermore, even when an egg furnished with an endodermal nucleus yielded an abnormal embryo lacking organized ectodermal tissues, *some specific ectodermal cell types—i.e., neurons, skin cells, etc.—were present.* Thus, the genetic information required to produce these cells had still been retained in the endodermal nucleus even though the normal or-

Fig. 9-3. Transplantation of embryonic nuclei.

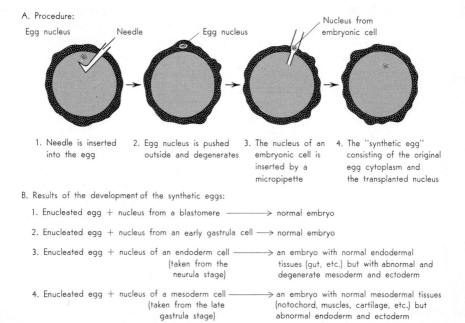

A. Procedure:

Egg nucleus   Needle   Egg nucleus   Nucleus from embryonic cell

1. Needle is inserted into the egg
2. Egg nucleus is pushed outside and degenerates
3. The nucleus of an embryonic cell is inserted by a micropipette
4. The "synthetic egg" consisting of the original egg cytoplasm and the transplanted nucleus

B. Results of the development of the synthetic eggs:

1. Enucleated egg + nucleus from a blastomere ——→ normal embryo

2. Enucleated egg + nucleus from an early gastrula cell ——→ normal embryo

3. Enucleated egg + nucleus of an endoderm cell ——→ an embryo with normal endodermal (taken from the neurula stage) tissues (gut, etc.) but with abnormal and degenerate mesoderm and ectoderm

4. Enucleated egg + nucleus of a mesoderm cell ——→ an embryo with normal mesodermal tissues (taken from the late gastrula stage) (notochord, muscles, cartilage, etc.) but abnormal endoderm and ectoderm

ganization of these cells into tissue could not be accomplished. Considering the many opportunities for nonspecific damage to the nuclei during transplantation and adaptation to the new cytoplasmic environment, the failure to obtain a high proportion of embryos normal in all respects is not surprising. As in the case of the dog that is a ventriloquist, you're not so much impressed with the fact that he does it well as that he does it at all.

A particularly convincing example of genetic retention is offered by the tobacco plant. Tobacco is subject to affliction with *crown gall tumors* induced by the presence of a bacterium called *Agrobacterium tumefaciens*. Some of these tumors are *terratomas* (tumors containing differentiated cell types found in normal tissues but chaotically arranged). Single cells resembling the parenchyma of normal plants were isolated from such tumors by micromanipulation and cultivated in nutrient media. Masses of their progeny were grafted to the stems of healthy plants and these masses ultimately produced normal shoots and leaves, flowered, and set seeds. The seeds when sown yielded normal healthy plants. Corresponding studies utilizing the progeny of single somatic cells and cell groups from normal carrot plants have yielded identical results. Thus at least some somatic cells not destined to become part of the germ line still retain all the genetic information needed for the production of a complete tobacco or carrot plant.

To summarize, then, the question of genetic retention by at least some differentiated cells has been proven in the tobacco and carrot plants, but still remains largely open in other systems. It is one of the most fertile subjects of investigation for the near future. My feeling, however, is that the questions will have to be reduced to very specific levels in order to become more fruitful. For instance, we might ask whether the DNA of a brain neuron possesses an intact gene for the production of hemoglobin which may even function to produce hemoglobin in the right environment. It should be possible to answer this and similar questions definitively in the next few years.

DIFFERENTIAL GENE ACTION AS THE BASIS OF CELLULAR DIFFERENTIATION

Let us now return to the first of the alternatives posed previously: namely that when a cell differentiates, its genetic constitution (i.e., its DNA) remains intact and unchanged, but, as a result of environmental alterations, corresponding changes occur in its other cell constituents.

Ultimately a mechanism of this kind must depend on the existence of *differential gene action* (the active functioning of some genes but not others at any given time). To make this clear consider the following model. Imagine a cell with a single chromosome bearing three genes. These genes direct the synthesis of three different proteins. The proteins may be enzymes like amylase or structural proteins like keratin. Figure 9-4 is a schematic description of possible functional changes in this cell during differentiation. At stage I, certain environmental conditions prevent gene A from functioning but permit genes B and C to do so. Therefore protein A is absent but B and C are present. At stage II gene A is activated and protein A makes its appearance. This eventually leads to stage III in which gene C is caused to stop functioning and protein C is no longer made. Now, if the previously made protein C is destroyed or released by the cell or rendered inactive in some fashion, the entire course of the differentiation will have encompassed at least two changes in the protein composition of the cell and have thereby altered its biological activity significantly.

According to this model then, the transition during red blood cell development from an erythroblast to a normoblast would not involve any changes in the DNA but would specifically involve (among other events) the switching on of the hemoglobin genes so that they could function thereafter, and perhaps the switching off of others so that they could not.

Fig. 9-4. A schematic model of differential gene action.

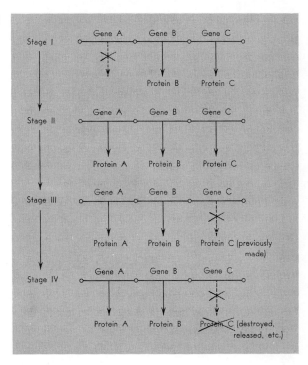

As is the case for *genetic retention,* present experimental evidence does not permit us to state conclusively that *differential gene action* does or does not play a role during cellular differentiation. But we are in a position at least to understand the biochemical levels at which the actions of genes can be controlled.

Specific Control of Gene Function

The following discussion is a brief review of the currently accepted mechanism by which genes direct the synthesis of proteins. Although gaps still exist in our knowledge, the main steps have been explored. They are illustrated schematically in Fig. 9-5.

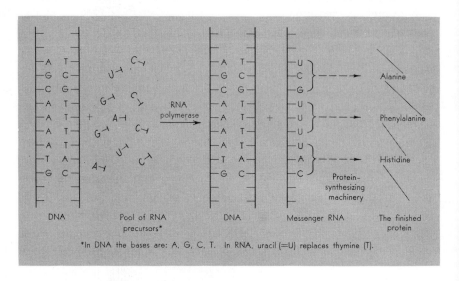

Fig. 9-5. A schematic model of protein synthesis.

I. THE GENE (DNA).   As mentioned previously, the sequence of bases in the DNA ultimately specifies the order of the amino acids in the fabricated protein.

II. MESSENGER RNA.   We believe that the information stored in the DNA is transcribed by synthesizing a molecule of RNA whose base sequence is a *copy of one of the DNA strands.* This is accomplished by an enzyme called RNA polymerase. The finished product, a single strand of RNA, is termed the *messenger,* and it serves as the pattern for fabricating the protein.

III. THE PROTEIN-SYNTHESIZING MACHINERY. This term includes a number of components which will not be described individually here.* The messenger RNA becomes bound to one or more particles called *ribosomes* and it is at these sites that actual protein fabrication occurs. Each successive set of three bases along the messenger RNA chain stands for a particular amino acid. (As shown in Fig. 9-5, UCG stands for alanine, UAC for histidine, etc.) The amino acid corresponding to each successive triplet of bases is brought to the messenger RNA-ribosome complex and is hooked to the neighboring amino acid. Thus the protein chain is synthesized, one amino acid at a time, according to the sequence of bases along the length of the messenger RNA. *The protein-synthesizing machinery* (i.e., the ribosomes plus the components needed to bring the amino acids into conjunction and bind them together) is employed in common for the synthesis of *all proteins. Only the molecules of messenger RNA are employed uniquely, each for the synthesis of a particular protein.*

Levels of Specific Control

Since each messenger RNA is a unique product of a single gene, efforts to control the function of a specific gene must be focused on its messenger. One can imagine two such levels of control, which are illustrated schematically in Fig. 9-6.

Level I. Gene A serves as the pattern for the synthesis of messenger A but gene B is prevented from doing so. Because no messenger B exists, protein B cannot be made.

* See Bonner and Mills, *Heredity, 2nd ed.,* McElroy, *Cell Physiology and Biochemistry, 2nd ed.,* and Swanson, *The Cell, 2nd ed.* (all Englewood Cliffs, N. J.: Prentice-Hall, 1964) for descriptions.

Fig. 9-6. Possible levels of control over gene action.

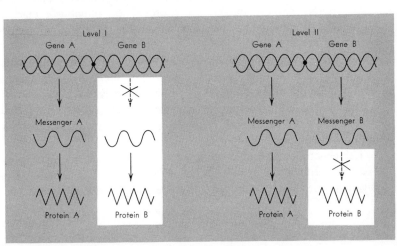

Level II. Both genes A and B are allowed to serve as patterns for the synthesis of their respective messengers. But only messenger A is utilized by the protein-synthesizing machinery to make protein A while messenger B is either not utilized at all or destroyed before it can be.

The problem of the level at which genes are "switched on or off" and the chemical details of the control mechanisms that do the switching is one of the most exciting in modern biology and is the subject of current investigation. Thus, right now we can do no more than provide a picture of this area, as yet devoid of details.

AN EXAMPLE OF SPECIFIC CONTROL OVER PROTEIN SYNTHESIS—ENZYME INDUCTION

The bacterium *Escherichia coli* can utilize a variety of compounds as sources of carbon and energy. These include simple sugars like glucose and galactose, disaccharides like lactose and sucrose, and other compounds like glycerol, succinic acid, etc. Lactose (glucose(1,4)-β-galactoside) is first split by *E. coli* into its constituent sugars, glucose and galactose, and these are further degraded to provide the raw material and energy for growth. The enzyme that catalyzes the first reaction is called *lactase,* or, more properly, *β-galactosidase.*

When *E. coli* is grown in the absence of lactose, it contains only traces of β-galactosidase (an average of about 1–5 molecules per cell and most cells don't have any). But after exposure to lactose the enzyme is synthesized from its constituent amino acids at a rapid rate, ultimately reaching a level as high as 5000 molecules per cell; this amounts to as much as 7 per cent of the dry weight of the cell! So long as lactose is present, the bacteria continue to make β-galactosidase rapidly and the level of enzyme remains high. But if lactose is removed, they cease making the enzyme within minutes. As these cells continue to grow and multiply (if given another carbon and energy source), the previously made enzyme eventually disappears and ultimately returns to the low level of 1–5 molecules per cell.

The process described above is termed *enzyme induction.* Enzymes like β-galactosidase are said to be *inducible,* and lactose is called an *inducer.* Many inducible systems are now known to exist in a variety of microorganisms. Several examples of enzyme induction have also been demonstrated in animal cells, both in the intact organisms and in tissue and dispersed cell culture.

The genetic control of β-galactosidase synthesis in *E. coli* represents an excellent illustration of differential gene action. The *structural gene* for β-galactosidase—i.e., the gene that determines the order of the amino acids in this protein—has been located on the *E. coli* chromosome. It is symbolized by the letter "Z." Right next to it is a second gene called "i." It is a *regulatory gene*. That is to say, it determines whether the Z gene can or cannot function. The relationship between the two is illustrated schematically in Fig. 9-7.

When lactose is not present, it is believed that the i-gene (acting in a manner as yet unknown) prevents the Z-gene from serving as a pattern for the synthesis of its messenger RNA. Because no messenger exits, β-galactosidase cannot be synthesized. When lactose is present, however, it interferes with the activity of the i-gene, again in a manner as yet unknown. Consequently the Z-gene is released from control and can now function, i.e., serve as a pattern for messenger synthesis. Hence, β-galactosidase can now be synthesized in large amounts. Because the messenger RNA is very unstable (at least in *E. coli* and other bacteria) and can make only a few molecules of enzyme before being destroyed, the Z-gene must function continually, turning out messenger RNA in order to maintain a high level of enzyme synthesis. Hence, if lactose is now removed, the i-gene can once again act to prevent the Z-gene from functioning, wipe out the supply of its messenger and thereby stop the synthesis of β-galactosidase within a few minutes. Please note that this method of control corresponds to "level I" shown in Fig. 9-6.

In the past few years many regulatory genes have been detected in microorganisms. Each controls the activity of one (and sometimes more than one) structural gene. Whether regulatory genes exist in the cells of

Fig. 9-7. The control of β-galactoside synthesis in E. coli.

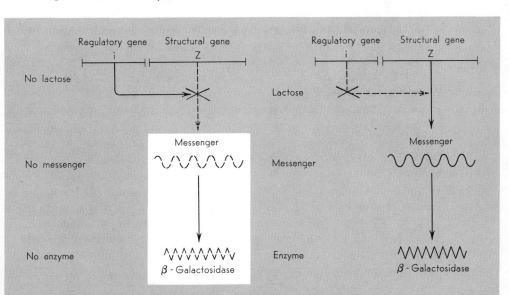

higher organisms and whether they play a role in cellular differentiation are two of the most exciting questions now being investigated.

DIFFERENTIAL ACTIVITY OF CHROMOSOMES
DURING DEVELOPMENT:
THE GIANT CHROMOSOMES OF INSECTS

Certain tissue cells of insects contain giant chromosomes that correspond in number and shape to those in their germ cells except for being tremendously larger. This is due to the fact that the giant chromosomes are made up of large bundles of DNA strands adhering to each other longitudinally. It is believed that giant chromosomes arise by repeated duplication of the DNA along the entire chromosomal length. In ordinary cells such duplications are followed by mitosis, but in these special tissues the duplicated DNA remains together, hence the chromosomal enlargement. The giant chromosomes in the salivary glands of the fruit fly represent a choice example, familiar now to generations of biology students, but the same phenomenon is observed in many other tissues including those of the midgut, rectum, malphighian tubules, etc.

Figure 9-8 shows a giant chromosome from the salivary gland of a moth, *Chironomus*. The rings are due to local irregularities in the physical structure of the DNA (i.e., changes in thickness due to local coiling of the strands, etc.). Because the DNA strands are lined up coincidentally, these minute irregularities become visible in the microscope as rings.

Chromosome Puffs

As seen in Fig. 9-8, most of the rings are discrete and sharp but others are diffuse, and in these regions the chromosome is puffed out. Experimental evidence indicates that, in the puffed regions, the DNA strands are not tightly coiled (like springs) and compressed together but are uncoiled and extended. *Furthermore these regions appear to be particularly active in synthesizing RNA.* The RNA produced there has been shown to migrate out of the nucleus into the surrounding cytoplasm and to become associated with the ribosomes. It is tempting to presume that this is messenger RNA and that the puffed regions are extraordinarily active sites of messenger synthesis.

DIFFERENTIAL CHANGES IN PUFFING. Two kinds of differential changes have been observed to occur in the puffing patterns of giant chromosomes:

1. *Tissue-specific puffs:* If at any one time in the life of an insect we compare the giant chromosomes of different tissues, we find patterns of puffing specific for each tissue. That is to say, the same regions will

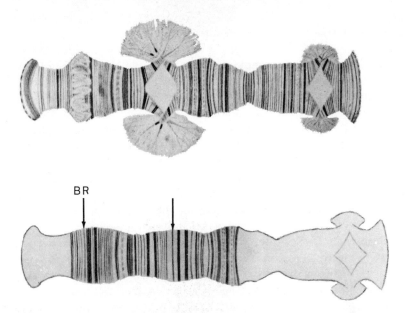

BR

Fig. 9-8. (A) Chromosome 4 from the salivary gland of Chironomus tentans. (B) The same chromosome showing two typical puffs. Note particularly that the banding pattern can be followed into the smaller subdivisions of the chromosome; the origin of the puffs can be traced to single bands in the unexpanded chromosome (BR1 and BR2 in A). (From Beerman.)

always be puffed in a particular salivary gland chromosome at a certain stage of the insect's life and completely different regions will be puffed in the corresponding chromosome of the midgut tissue cells at the same stage. *Each such region corresponds to a gene or small group of genes and may well be a reflection of the possibility that, at any given time, different genes are particularly active in different tissues.*

2. *Time-specific puffs:* If we now examine the same tissue at intervals during the life cycle of the insect, we find that puffs appear and disappear in the various regions of the chromosomes in a regular, reproducible pattern. *This may well be a reflection of the possibility that as a cell proceeds along a pathway of differentiation and during the course of its functional existence, different genes are particularly active at different times.*

RÉSUMÉ

In these last two chapters we have tried to make clear the following premises:

1. That cellular differentiation is just another way of saying that the phenotype of a cell has changed, i.e., that it has become different functionally and/or morphologically from its parent and/or sister cells and from what it once was.

111

2. That, unlike the simple unique phenotypic changes seen in primitive microorganisms, which involve the gain or loss of a single enzyme, a differentiating cell experiences a complex, programmed sequence of changes that occur in a definite chronological order.

3. That differentiation may in some cases result from stable changes in the genetic constitution of the cell. In no case, however, has this been demonstrated, and in some cases it has been disproven.

4. That cell differentiation may be the result of differential gene activity, the consequence of specific controls exerted on the synthesis of messenger RNA by the genes and on the subsequent use of those messages for the synthesis of proteins (and on the activities of the proteins themselves). In no case, though, have these mechanisms been demonstrated conclusively no matter how likely they may appear to be.

5. That this is one of the most exciting areas of investigation in modern biology, the immediate task being to get to the molecular basis of these phenotypic changes and to understand how they are controlled temporally, quantitatively, and spatially.

SELECTED READINGS

The back issues of *Scientific American* contain a host of interestingly written articles, some of which cover topics mentioned in this book. The beginning student can gain much esthetic enjoyment as well as information by their perusal.

A profound examination of the more modern aspects of developmental biology, particularly at the molecular level, might well be delayed until the student has acquired the background in physical science, mathematics, genetics, and biochemistry needed for full appreciation. In the meantime it is valuable to become fully conversant with the classical foundations of the subject for it is from these that the research problems of the present and future spring. The following books are useful in these respects.

Waddington, C. H., *Principles of Embryology*. London: Allen & Unwin, 1956. A good elementary text.

Willier, B. H., P. A. Weiss and V. Hamburger, *Analysis of Development*. Philadelphia: Saunders, 1955. A comprehensive advanced treatise that may serve as a sourcebook for further readings.

Wilson, E. B., *The Cell in Development and Heredity*. New York: Macmillan, 1925. A true classic written by one of the giants of twentieth century biology, as fresh and illuminating as if it had been written yesterday.

Index

114